MACMILLAN **EXAMS**

Ready for
First

workbook with key

3rd Edition

Roy Norris

with Lynda Edwards

with audio CD

Updated in line with Cambridge English: First (FCE) 2015 revisions

Macmillan Education Limited
4 Crinan Street
London N1 9XW

Companies and representatives throughout the world

ISBN 978-0-230-44008-1 (+ key)
ISBN 978-0-230-44009-8 (- key)

Designed by xen
Illustrated by Stephen Elford, Jim Kane and Robin Lawrie
Cover photograph: **Getty Images**/Graham Monro/gm photographics
Picture research by Victoria Gaunt

Author's acknowledgements
Special thanks to the freelance editor.

The publishers would like to thank all those who participated in the
development of the project.

The authors and publishers would like to thank the following for
permission to reproduce their photographs:
Alamy/Kevin Britland p4, Alamy/OOK Die Bildagentur der Fotografen
GmbH p12, Alamy/tech gadgets p33, Alamy/Stuart Kelly p105, Alamy/
Jeff Morgan 08 p56, Alamy/Dale O'Dell p68, Alamy/Alistair Scott p76;
Camera Press p9;
Comstock p27(coffee machine);
Corbis p65, Corbis/Monty Rakusen/cultura p37;
Faber & Faber Ltd p28;
FLPA/Mike Lane p100(r);
Getty Images pp27(remote),29,44,57,128, Getty Images/De Agostini
p122, Getty Images/Don Farrall p84(b), Getty Images/Rich Legg p41,
Getty Images/Holger Leue p60, Getty/mother image p120, Getty
Images/Popperfoto p25(t), Getty Images/SSPL p64,
Imagesource pp27(hairdryer),81, Imagesource/Fstop p124,
Imagesource/GretaMarie p121;
Macmillan Australia p27(iron);
Rex Features/Jonathan Hordle p84(t), Rex Features/Christopher
Jones p92, Rex Features/Geoffrey Swaine p117;
Science Photo Library/Ria Novosti p17;
Superstock/Junior p100(l), Superstock/Latitude p5, Superstock/Pixtal
p108;
Thinkstock/istockphoto pp20(laptop, e-book, bread machine, washing
machine), 25.

The authors and publishers are grateful for permission to reprint the
following copyright material:
Adapted material from article 'A night at the Oscars' first appeared
in The Week dated 04.02.12, reprinted by permission of Dennis
Publishing;
Extracted material from article 'Sydney Chaplin: the silent star the
world forgot' first appeared in The Week dated 25.10.03, reprinted by
permission of Independent Print Limited;
Article 'I Want Your Job: Air Traffic Controller' by author Alex McRae,
copyright © Alex McRae 2006 first appeared in The Independent
12.10.06, reprinted by permission of the publisher;

Article 'The worst ways to lose your wad' by Simon Calder, copyright
© Simon Calder 1999, first appeared in The Independent 03.07.99,
reprinted by permission of the publisher;
Article 'Innovative shop Unpackaged is at the forefront of a consumer
revolution' by Gillian Orr, copyright © Gillian Orr 2012, first appeared
in The Independent 19.12.12 reprinted by permission of the
publisher;
Article 'The truth behind body language' by Karen Hainsworth,
copyright © Karen Hainsworth 2005, first appeared in The
Independent 27.10.05, reprinted by permission of the publisher;
Adapted material from article 'Help, I'm doing 135mph and can't
stop' by Thair Shaikh, copyright © Thair Shaikh 2006, first appeared
in The Independent 11.03.06, reprinted by permission of the
publisher;
Adapted material from article 'A Life in the Day: Paolo Fazioli' by
Norman Beedie, copyright © Norman Beedie 2002, first appeared in
The Sunday Times Magazine 17.11.02, reprinted by permission of
News International;
Adapted material from article 'Best of Times, Worst of Times: Jo
Brand' by Sue Fox, copyright © Sue Fox 2005, first appeared in The
Sunday Times Magazine 22.05.05, reprinted by permission of News
International;
Adapted material from article 'A writer's life: G P Taylor' first
appeared in The Daily Telegraph 08.05.06, reprinted by permission of
the publisher;
Adapted material from article 'Striking Mom, Jessica Stilwell refuses
to clean up after 'disgusting' children' by Nick Allen, copyright ©
Nick Allen 2012, first appeared in The Daily Telegraph 11.10.12,
reprinted by permission of the publisher;
Article 'Wizard way to Oz' by Jan Etherington, copyright © Jan
Etherington 2006, first appeared in The Daily Telegraph 30.08.06,
reprinted by permission of the publisher;
Adapted material from article 'Ageing Atlantic raft adventures arrive in
Caribbean to cheers' by David Harrison, copyright © David Harrison
2011, first appeared in The Daily Telegraph 09.04.11, reprinted by
permission of the publisher;
Adapted material from article 'Brazil prisoners reading books to
shorten their sentences', first appeared in The Daily Telegraph
26.06.12, reprinted by permission of the publisher;
Adapted material from article 'I ate well every day of my life until I
came to England' by Elfreda Pownall, copyright © Elfreda Pownall
2012, first appeared in The Daily Telegraph 09.10.12, reprinted by
permission of the publisher;
Adapted material from article 'Interview: Graeme Black, fashion
designer' by Ruth Walker, copyright © Ruth Walker 2012, first
appeared on website www.scotsman.com, 23.09.12 reprinted by
permission of the publisher;
Adapted material from article 'Just a load of hot air' by Tom Kelly,
copyright © Tom Kelly 2006, first appeared in The Daily Mail
08.05.06, reprinted by permission of Solo Syndication.

These materials may contain links for third party websites. We have
no control over, and are not responsible for, the contents of such
third party websites. Please use care when accessing them.

Although we have tried to trace and contact copyright holders before
publication, in some cases this has not been possible. If contacted
we will be pleased to rectify any errors or omissions at the earliest
opportunity.

Printed and bound in Poland by CGS

2025 2024 2023 2022 2021
24 23 22 21 20 19 18

Contents

1 Lifestyle 4

2 High energy 12

3 A change for the better? 20

4 A good story 28

5 Doing what you have to 36

6 Relative relationships 44

7 Value for money 52

8 Up and away 60

9 Mystery and imagination 68

10 Nothing but the truth 76

11 What on earth's going on? 84

12 Looking after yourself 92

13 Animal magic 100

14 Mind your language 108

Listening bank 116

Phrasal verb list 130

Lexical phrase list 133

Irregular verb list 135

Answer key 137

① Lifestyle

Multiple matching

1 You are going to read an article in which four people talk about their lifestyles. For questions **1–10**, choose from the people (**A–D**). The people may be chosen more than once.

Which person says the following?

I have become more flexible in my work.	**1** B
I could not imagine having a different lifestyle.	**2** A
It is difficult to form and maintain close friendships.	**3** B
I do not feel as if I am working.	**4** C
My lifestyle suits my personality.	**5** D
The nature of my living space often leads to tensions.	**6** A
Some people are surprised by my choice of lifestyle.	**7** D
I try not to accumulate personal belongings.	**8** C
Travelling makes it easy to get jobs.	**9** B
Many of my ancestors had the same kind of lifestyle.	**10** A

A nomadic lifestyle

We hear from four people for whom travel is an important part of their lives.

A Dougie

I come from a long line of travelling showmen, and for most of the year we tour the country from fairground to fairground. It's been in my family's blood for nearly two centuries. There was someone on my father's side who used to train bears, and another relative who lost a finger working as the assistant to a knife-thrower.

I live in a caravan, with my wife, Janie, and the two kids, and because conditions are a bit cramped, we get on each other's nerves quite a lot. Everyone works really hard; we have to set up all our heavy equipment – usually in the middle of the night – then we're on our feet for hours on end every day for the duration of the fair. And after about a week or so we take it all down again, and move on to the next place. It's a tough life, but I don't see myself doing anything else – there's nothing else I'd rather do.

B Lucy

I've taught English in nine countries so far, including Spain, New Zealand, Jordan and now, Vietnam. Being prepared to move around means I never have problems finding work and I think it's helped me become a better teacher, too – I've learnt to adapt to different cultures and respond to the specific problems each type of learner has with the language.

The downside is that, although I've met and worked with a lot of different people, it's hard to get to know them really well, because I'm never in one country for more than a couple of years. We can, and do, keep in touch online, but that becomes fairly superficial after a while and I often lose contact with people.

C Phillip

As the financial director of a multinational company based in France, I spend my life travelling and I'm rarely in one place for more than six months. Home is England at the moment, but last month it was Milan and before that, Atlanta. I live in hotels or rent for short periods, so the sensation is one of being on permanent holiday.

Living nomadically has shaped my attitude to possessions; I do my best to keep them to the bare minimum and I don't get attached to things. If I have to buy something for a house, like furniture or curtains, I don't mind leaving it behind when I move on. I'm not sure how long I'll be able to go on with this lifestyle; I've spent the last twelve years focusing on my career and I'd quite like to settle down soon.

D Sally

I always wanted to travel and I like being on 5 my own, but I also enjoy towns and cities and spending time with other people. So I live and work my way around the country in a canal boat, stepping in and out of urban life as I choose. I earn my living as a one-woman theatre company, putting on shows for disabled children in the places I visit.

I'm very different from my parents; they still live in the house they bought when they got

married and we never travelled very far when I was growing up. So my old friends from childhood still think it's weird that I never spend more than a week or so in any one place. My only worry is that I'll find it hard to settle in the future. I'm a very restless type and living on a boat certainly satisfies that side of my nature.

2 The following extracts from the text contain expressions with the word *on*. Complete the extracts with words from the box.

end	feet	holiday	lifestyle	nerves	own	place	shows	side

1 There was someone **on my father's** _____ who used to train bears …

2 … we **get on each other's** _____ quite a lot.

3 … we're **on our** _____ **for hours on** _____ every day for the duration of the fair.

4 And after about a week or so we take it all down again, and **move on to the next** _____ .

5 … the sensation is one of being **on** permanent _____ .

6 I'm not sure how long I'll be able to **go on with this** _____ .

7 … I like being **on my** _____ , but I also enjoy … spending time with other people.

8 I earn my living as a one-woman theatre company, **putting on** _____ for disabled children …

3 Match the meanings **a–f** to the expressions from exercise **2**.

a related to my father _____*on my father's side*_____

b alone _____

c standing up for long periods at a time _____

d annoy one another _____

e organizing performances _____

f continue living like this _____

Vocabulary

Wordlist on page 205 of the Coursebook

A Lifestyle

Match the adjectives in the box to the different lifestyles **1–5**.

alternative	chaotic	healthy	luxurious	sedentary

1 There's nothing better than fruit and yoghurt after an early-morning run. _____

2 Expensive clothes, a huge house and exotic holidays – that's the life for me! _____

3 I spend so much time rushing around that I hardly have time to eat. _____

4 After working all day in front of the computer, I get home and collapse onto the sofa. _____

5 Jake lives on his own in a caravan on a remote Scottish island. _____

B Clothes

1 Use the clues below to complete the grid. When you have all the answers you will find an extra word for number 12 down.

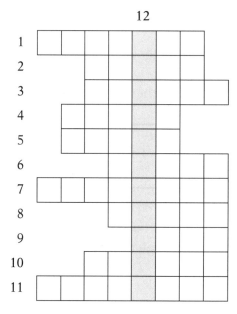

1 describes clothes which are untidy and dirty

2 a piece of cloth worn round the neck to keep you warm

3 describes clothes which are comfortable and suitable for informal situations

4 the opposite of *loose*

5 describes clothes which are simple in design with no decoration

6 these are worn on your feet inside your shoes

7 sports shoes

8 describes clothes which are very loose on your body

9 a narrow piece of leather or cloth worn round the waist

10 a hard hat worn by motorcyclists and soldiers to protect their head

11 a piece of jewellery which you wear round your wrist

2 Use one of the adjectives from the Wordlist on pages 205–206 of the Coursebook to describe the items of clothing **1–5**.

0   *a shabby overcoat*   **1** _____   **2** _____

3 _____   **4** _____   **5** _____

C *Get*

Lexical phrase list on page 133; Phrasal verb list on pages 130–132

1 Complete the sentences with words from the box to form a verb with *get*. The verb with *get* should have the same meaning as the verb or phrase in brackets.

away	back	by	off	out of	over	~~to~~

0 We didn't get ____*to*____ (arrive in) London until midnight.

1 I don't earn very much but I get _____ (manage to live) OK.

2 It took him a long time to get _____ (recover from) the flu.

3 What time do you think you'll get _____ (return)?

4 He was shot while trying to get _____ (escape) from the police.

5 You have to get _____ (leave) the bus at the shopping centre.

6 I can't seem to get _____ (stop) the habit of biting my nails.

2 Complete the sentences with appropriate words from the box.

exercise	impression	paid	ready	rid	touch	worse

1 I haven't written to Steve for ages – I really ought to get in _____ with him.

2 I think footballers get _____ far too much.

3 The car kept breaking down so we decided to get _____ of it.

4 I spent the day getting _____ for Christmas, buying presents and cooking.

5 My throat's getting _____ . I think I ought to see a doctor.

6 I got the _____ she was bored; she kept yawning all the time.

7 I'm going out on my bike; I need to get some _____ .

D Word combinations

1 Each pair of words can be used with one noun from the box. Match the nouns to **1–5**.

event	interview	~~jacket~~	life	party	premiere

0 dinner sports	_____*jacket*_____	**3** annual sporting	_____
1 political birthday	_____	**4** film world	_____
2 radio job	_____	**5** social private	_____

2 Complete the sentences with a word combination from exercise **1**.

1 The Olympic® Games is the only major _____ I ever watch on television.

2 I have three young children, so I don't have a _____ at the moment.

3 It's a formal event so I have to wear a _____ and a bow tie.

4 The _____ of this opera took place in London on June 16th.

5 The tennis star spoke about his knee injury during a recent _____ .

6 The prime minister is the leader of the country's main left-wing _____ .

Language focus

 Grammar reference on page 209 of the Coursebook

A Adverbs of frequency

In each of the following sentences, one of the adverbs or adverb phrases is in an incorrect position. Underline the incorrectly placed adverb or adverb phrase and rewrite the relevant part of the sentence.

0 I normally cycle to work but I <u>from time to time</u> walk, especially in summer.

but from time to time I walk

1 Always I set my alarm clock for seven o'clock, but usually I wake up before it goes off.

_____

2 I've hardly ever had a day off school and I never am late.

_____

3 I very often have a cup of tea mid-morning but rarely I drink it in the afternoon.

_____

4 My mum cooks once a week paella, but I don't normally eat very much of it.

_____

5 We sometimes go to France on holiday, but we never have been to Paris.

_____

B *Be used to, get used to* and *used to*

Write the words in the correct order to make sentences. Begin each sentence with the word in bold.

0 trouble / school? / **Did** / use / into / you / at / to / get

Did you use to get into trouble at school?

1 bike / school / to / to / to / a / **Lucy** / use / used / get

_____

2 got / used / morning / to / in / up / the / **She's** / getting / early

_____

3 every / dad / to / to / me / **My** / his / clean / Sunday / used / get / car

_____

4 paid / worked / didn't / much / waiter / he / as / to / a / when / use / **Paul** / get

_____

5 not / doing / are / people / **Many** / work / used / hard / young / to

_____

Reading and Use of English
Part 4

Transformations

Complete the second sentence so that it has a similar meaning to the first sentence, using the word given. **Do not change the word given.** You must use between **two** and **five** words, including the word given. There is an example at the beginning **(0)**. Write **only** the missing words **IN CAPITAL LETTERS**.

0 She often went abroad on holiday before she got married.
WOULD
She _____*WOULD OFTEN GO*_____ abroad on holiday before she got married.

1 I almost always go out on Saturday night.
EVER
I _____ at home on Saturday night.

2 We've been back at school for two weeks and I still find it hard to get up early.
USED
We've been back at school for two weeks and I'm still not
_____ up early.

3 I can't wait to go on holiday.
FORWARD
I'm really _____ on holiday.

4 I'm sorry I haven't written to you for such a long time.
TAKEN
I'm sorry it _____ long to write to you.

5 Anna rarely gets less than 70 per cent in her English exam.
RARE
It _____ get less than 70 per cent in her English exam.

6 Richard is normally very talkative so I'm surprised he was so quiet.
LIKE
I'm surprised that Richard didn't say very much because it's
_____ so quiet.

Reading and Use of English
Part 1

Multiple-choice cloze

For questions **1–8**, read the text below and decide which answer (**A**, **B**, **C** or **D**) best fits each gap. There is an example at the beginning (**0**).

Graeme Black

Scottish designer Graeme Black talks about how he became **(0)** ____ in fashion.

'I didn't have any contact with the fashion **(1)** ____ from within my family but I always wanted to design. My first real **(2)** ____ of understanding I wanted to be a designer was when I saw a Karl Lagerfeld fashion show on TV and was so excited by seeing the clothes, the girls – the whole world **(3)** ____ so exotic I was hooked. I then began to study **(4)** ____ so I could get into art school, doing every possible art, pottery, creative course to improve my **(5)** ____ of getting a place.'

Black was the **(6)** ____ boy in the sewing class at his school, soaking up knowledge and working with whatever fabrics he could lay his hands on. 'I once made a dress out of one of my mother's sheets. I tore it up into strips, then knotted it together to form a dress with a hand-painted back panel. I didn't **(7)** ____ my mother's permission and, yes, I did get into **(8)** ____ for ruining a perfectly good sheet.'

0 A keen	**B** enthusiastic	**C** interested	**D** fond
1 A industry	**B** affair	**C** style	**D** activity
2 A reminder	**B** remembrance	**C** memory	**D** souvenir
3 A resulted	**B** worked	**C** affected	**D** seemed
4 A much	**B** strong	**C** hard	**D** heavy
5 A occasions	**B** chances	**C** applications	**D** risks
6 A lonely	**B** own	**C** alone	**D** only
7 A ask	**B** demand	**C** look	**D** search
8 A blame	**B** fault	**C** trouble	**D** problem

Writing
Part 2

Informal letter and email

In Part 2 of the Writing paper of the *First* exam you may have to write a letter or an email. Some of the reasons for writing letters and emails are given in the table below.

1 Read sentences **1–10** and decide if each one is formal or informal. Then write the number of the sentence in the correct column in the table below.

	Formal	Informal
Complaining		
Asking for information	*1*	
Giving information		
Apologizing		
Giving advice		

1 Could you please also <u>inform</u> me of the exact dates you would require me to work if I were accepted for the job.

2 <u>You really shouldn't</u> buy anything in the markets there – it's all poor-quality stuff and far too expensive.

3 Please accept my sincere apologies <u>for the delay in responding to you</u>.

4 <u>And</u> I do think the hotel could have organized some kind of bus service – it took us ages to get to the beach every day!

5 <u>I have a wide range of experience in working</u> with children, including a two-month period spent as an assistant at an international summer camp.

6 I'm really sorry <u>it's taken me so long to get back to you</u> – I've just been so busy lately.

7 <u>Moreover</u>, when the food eventually arrived, the fish was undercooked and we had to ask one of your waiters to take it back to the kitchen.

8 Owing to the high frequency of thefts in the area, <u>we would strongly advise you not to</u> carry large amounts of cash with you.

9 <u>I've done loads of jobs in hotels</u> so you can believe me when I tell you that the work is often very stressful.

10 Can you <u>let me know</u> what time you think you'll be arriving?

2 Look at the words and expressions that have been underlined in exercise **1**. Match each formal word or expression with its informal equivalent and write them both in the table.

Formal	Informal
1 *inform me*	10 *let me know*

Informal letter

Informal letter: pages 14 and 15 of the Coursebook

1 Read the following Part 2 instructions.

This is part of a letter you have received from your English friend, Jim.

> I'm really looking forward to staying with you just after Christmas. What kinds of things do you normally do then? What plans do you have for when I'm there? Please let me know what the weather will be like and if there are any special clothes I should take.
>
> Thanks
>
> Jim

Write your **letter** in **140–190** words.

2 The letter should contain the information in **a–c**. Match **a–c** to paragraphs **1–3** of the letter below. Write the correct letters next to the paragraphs.

a the kinds of things you normally do at that time

b the type of weather he can expect and clothes he should bring

c the plans you have for when he comes to stay

	Dear Jim
Beginning	Thanks a lot for your letter – we're really looking forward to your visit as well. We talk about it all the time!
Paragraph 1	We normally spend the period just after Christmas relaxing at home and getting over all the celebrations. We either read or play games, and occasionally we go out for a walk in the snow.
Paragraph 2	When you're here, though, we'd like to take you to the mountains for a couple of days. We've rented a small apartment in a lovely area about an hour's drive away. We can go cross-country skiing during the day and in the evenings we can try out different restaurants. The area is famous for its good food. We'll come back to the city on the 31st and celebrate New Year's Eve at home.
Paragraph 3	The temperature drops to minus 10° in December, so make sure you bring some warm clothes. A pair of walking boots would be ideal, as well as some waterproof trousers – just in case you fall over in the snow!
Ending	That's all for now, then. We'll see you at the airport on the 27th.
	Best wishes
	Katrin

3 Write your own letter to a British friend who is coming to stay with you for the first time for **a week in August**. Include the same points, **a**, **b** and **c**, as in the letter above and follow the same paragraph plan. Write your **letter** in **140–190** words.

Don't forget!

Plan your letter before you write it. Use some of the informal language and linkers from page 14 of the Coursebook.

Gapped text

1 You are going to read an interview with Paolo Fazioli, who makes pianos. Six sentences have been removed from the article. Choose from the sentences **A–G** the one which fits each gap (**1–6**). There is one extra sentence which you do not need to use.

A Life in the Day:
Paolo Fazioli

Paolo Fazioli makes some of the world's most sought-after pianos. His concert grands cost around £80,000. He lives close to his factory in Sacile, near Venice. By Norman Beedie

I start the day with orange juice, two kiwi fruits, vitamins, weak coffee with milk and biscuits, before driving in my green BMW 530 to the factory. Building the best piano I possibly can: that is my passion, my life's work.

I started studying piano late, but I obtained the diploma in piano from the Conservatorio di Pesaro. I had an engineering degree, too. And because my father was in the furniture and wood industry, it seemed obvious to me what my career must be. I knew there was a gap in the market, for as a pianist I had never found a piano I was happy with. **1** So I started from scratch. I rebuilt that piano 17 times before I was happy.

Now I have my own factory, I do as I please. I spend eight hours a day in the workshop, and if I see a change that needs to be made, I can make it straightaway. **2**

Each piano is born, like a human being, with its own unique character. It is the combination of good materials and good construction that gives the best results. **3** For this we use the red spruce, sometimes called 'the tree of music'. I like to choose the trees myself, in the Val de Fiemme forest. These are 150-year-old trees, descended from the ones Stradivarius used for his violins, and only one in 200 will have the natural resonance I am looking for.

4 But first the wood must rest for up to a year, so that any tension in it disappears. A piano's case, too, is important. It must be very solid, with 8 to 10 layers glued together. Then there is the iron frame – the iron and wood work against each other with a beauty that is fundamental. A piano has thousands of working parts and the strings

must be able to bear 20 tonnes of tension. Then there are 88 keys to be balanced, the hammers to be 'voiced' and the strings tuned.

My 35 workers take hours over each detail, like spinning copper round steel for the strings. **5** Last year we made about 90 pianos – our best since we started in 1980, but 120 would be our maximum. Quality is my only interest.

My staff go home for lunch with their families. They are important to me. We are like a family. Sometimes, when we have made a special piano, perhaps with a beautiful inlaid case, my workers ask me if they can invite their friends in to look at it. So on Sundays the factory is open to their friends and families. Maybe 100 to 150 will come. **6**

In the evening my colleagues and I often eat out. I like simple food: spaghetti alla carbonara, or with basil sauce. I sleep well. Because, you know, when you have such an intensive day, then you sleep like a log.

A First we choose the wood for the sounding board, the heart of the piano – the flat board which lies under the strings.

B I hand them the key and leave them to it.

C I saw I must build my own, and I knew that if I built a piano that pleased me, it would sell.

D To do this they take only the finest quality wood and always under my supervision.

E It will take two years for that tree to become a piano.

F With the big firms, to make even a small alteration can take years of discussions and meetings.

G A machine could do this in minutes, but when they do it by hand I know the result will be perfect.

2 In the two sentences from the text below the word *hand* is used both as a noun and as a verb. Complete **1–6** with a part of the body from the box. The word required in **a** and **b** is the same.

*When they do it by **hand**, I know the result will be perfect.*

*I **hand** them the key and leave them to it.*

arm	eye	face	foot	head	mouth

1 a He's a reasonable footballer but he can't _____ **the ball** very well.

  b The person in charge of a school is known as the _____ **teacher**.

2 a The _____ **of a storm** or a hurricane is the centre of it.

  b His dirty clothes and scruffy appearance caused the policewoman to _____ him **suspiciously**.

3 a They found her lying unconscious **at the** _____ **of the stairs on the ground floor**.

  b Taxpayers shouldn't have to _____ **the bill for** repairs to the palace – the royal family should pay for them.

4 a It's my belief that if you _____ **the police**, more criminals will carry guns.

  b They walked along _____ **in** _____ .

5 a When she reads, she'll often _____ **the words** without actually saying them.

  b The _____ **of a river** is the place where it flows out into the sea.

6 a Most of the rooms in the hotel _____ **the sea**.

  b We've only ever spoken on the phone – we've never met _____ **to** _____ .

Vocabulary

Wordlist on page 206 of the Coursebook

A Music

1 Write the names of the musical instruments.

1 _____

2 _____

3 _____

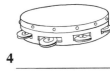

4 _____

5 _____

6 _____

7 _____

8 _____

2 Complete the sentences with words from the box.

| charts | lead | session | song | tune | wind |

1 She's miming that _____ – her mouth isn't moving in time with the words.

2 I have to write the names of five _____ instruments. So far I've got flute, trumpet and saxophone.

3 This album was number one in the _____ for 15 consecutive weeks.

4 They cancelled the concert because the _____ vocalist had lost his voice.

5 My uncle's a _____ musician; he's played keyboards for loads of different bands on their albums.

6 Dad, it is not a horrible noise and their instruments are in _____ ! You just don't understand music.

B Sport

1 Write the words for the people who do each of the following sports.

0	surfing	_surfer_	**5**	gymnastics	_____
1	athletics	_____	**6**	skiing	_____
2	basketball	_____	**7**	snowboarding	_____
3	cycling	_____	**8**	tennis	_____
4	golf	_____			

2 Match the sports in column A with the places in column B.

A		B
1 motor-racing	_circuit_	rink
2 football	_____	court
3 athletics	_____	slope
4 ski	_____	pool
5 swimming	_____	track
6 golf	_____	pitch
7 tennis	_____	~~circuit~~
8 ice-skating	_____	course

3 Choose the best answer (**A**, **B**, **C** or **D**) to complete the sentences.

1 He was given a full set of golf _____ as a retirement present.

  A bats   **B** clubs   **C** sticks   **D** posts

2 Only five seconds separated the winner from the _____ in this year's marathon.

  A opponent   **B** failure   **C** loser   **D** runner-up

3 Olympiakos _____ 0–0 with Chelsea in the first leg of the semi-final in Athens.

  A drew   **B** equalled   **C** equalized   **D** shared

4 Second Division football _____ get paid very little in my country.

  A judges   **B** arbitrators   **C** referees   **D** umpires

5 We are expecting over 300 surfers to take _____ in this year's surfing championship.

  A place   **B** up   **C** part   **D** competition

6 I've never really enjoyed _____ sport.

  A going in   **B** taking up   **C** making   **D** doing

7 The home side _____ 76–75 in a thrilling game of basketball.

   A won   **B** beat   **C** scored   **D** marked

8 The players were cheered by their _____ as they came off the pitch.

   A audience   **B** supporters   **C** viewers   **D** public

C Word formation

Use the word given in capitals at the end of some of the lines to form a word that fits in the space in the same line. All of the words require a prefix.

1 Most of what you've written in your answer has nothing to do with the question and is therefore _____ .   **RELEVANT**

2 There was some _____ about who should be captain and it took quite a while to reach a decision.   **AGREE**

3 You obviously _____ when I set the homework. You've done the wrong exercise.   **UNDERSTAND**

4 He claimed he had won the lottery, but most people who knew him suspected he had obtained the money _____ .   **HONEST**

5 Derek is so _____ . You can never trust him to arrive on time for anything.   **RELY**

6 His childish and _____ behaviour often gets him into trouble at school.   **MATURE**

7 I keep telling you you're _____ ; those trousers are far too tight for you now!   **WEIGH**

8 The potatoes are _____ ; you should have boiled them for a bit longer.   **COOK**

9 The parents, who had left the two young children alone in the house, were accused of behaving _____ .   **RESPONSIBLE**

10 He always asks me what I think he should do. He seems _____ of making his own decisions.   **CAPABLE**

Language focus

Grammar reference on pages 209–210 of the Coursebook

A Indirect ways of asking questions

Write the words in the correct order to make sentences.

1 doing / have / me / been / you / telling / what / recently

   Would you mind _____ ?

2 something / can / cold / drink / where / I / to / get

   Does anybody know _____ ?

3 party / time / week / the / are / what / you / coming / to / next

   Could you tell me _____ ?

4 homework / did / the / not / me / you / to / do / why

   Could you explain to me _____ ?

5 interested / Friday / playing / if / in / on / are / tennis / you

   We'd like to know _____ .

6 he / living / does / a / for / what

   I wonder _____ .

B Gerunds and infinitives

Complete the sentences with either the infinitive with *to* or the gerund form of the word in brackets.

1 I don't mind _____ (look) after the neighbour's cat for a week, but I refuse _____ (have) it here in the house.

2 At first I was really keen on the idea of _____ (learn) _____ (speak) Swahili, but now I'm beginning _____ (think) it's a bit of a waste of time.

3 There appeared _____ (be) no one in the house. Pickering considered _____ (climb) through one of the open windows but if he did this, he risked _____ (attract) the attention of the neighbours. He decided _____ (wait) until it was dark.

4 Please stop _____ (make) so much noise. I'm trying _____ (concentrate).

5 I really don't feel like _____ (go) out tonight. I'd prefer _____ (stay) in and watch a film.

6 _____ (give) up chocolate is a good idea, but if you intend _____ (lose) ten kilos in three months, you'll have to do a lot more than that!

7 I'm delighted _____ (hear) you're coming to the wedding. Rachel and I are certainly both looking forward to _____ (see) you again.

8 I've been meaning _____ (paint) the front door for ages, but I keep _____ (forget) _____ (buy) the paint.

9 We'd really like _____ (live) in the city centre but it's virtually impossible _____ (find) a three-bedroom flat at a price we can afford _____ (pay).

10 I left school when I was 16 _____ (work) in my father's firm, but now I regret not _____ (go) to university.

C Open cloze: Prepositions

Complete the text with a suitable preposition in each gap. There is an example at the beginning (0).

What to expect in the exam

Prepositions are just one type of word you might have to write in the Open cloze task, which normally has 8 gaps.

Heavy musicians

I've never been particularly fond (0) _of_ heavy metal music, but my dad's a real fan. He used to go and see groups play (1) _____ concert all the time when he was a teenager, and when he found out that one of his favourite live bands, Black Purple, was going (2) _____ tour again, he just had to get tickets. I knew they'd had a few records (3) _____ the charts (4) _____ the seventies, and the two or three tracks I'd heard (5) _____ the radio didn't sound too bad, so when my dad asked me to go with him I agreed.

When they came (6) _____ stage I began to realize I'd made a big mistake. All the members of the band were (7) _____ least 60 years old, they all looked really out of condition and they produced some of the worst sounds I've ever heard. The guitarists were either extremely untalented or their instruments just weren't (8) _____ tune. The drummer looked completely uninterested (9) _____ everything and seemed to be playing the same beat over and over again. And as for the lead vocalist, he was quite good (10) _____ jumping up and down, but he certainly couldn't sing. I got fed up (11) _____ it all after about three songs and wanted to go home, but my dad made me stay (12) _____ the end.

Transformations

For questions **1–6**, complete the second sentence so that it has a similar meaning to the first sentence, using the word given. Do not change the word given. You must use between **two** and **five** words, including the word given. Write your answers **IN CAPITAL LETTERS**.

1 It's impossible for me not to laugh when he starts singing.
   HELP
   I can't _____ when he starts singing.

2 I really don't want to go out this evening.
   FEEL
   I really don't _____ out this evening.

3 Amy played much better than her opponent, so it was unfair that she lost the match.
   DESERVE
   Amy _____ the match, because she played much better than her opponent.

4 Rock stars often wear dark glasses so that people don't recognize them.
   PREVENT
   Rock stars often wear dark glasses _____ them.

5 It's obvious he shot himself in the foot by accident.
   MEAN
   He obviously _____ himself in the foot.

6 I hate it when I'm ill.
   STAND
   I _____ ill.

Multiple-choice cloze

For questions **1–8**, read the text below and decide which answer (**A, B, C** or **D**) best fits each gap. There is an example at the beginning **(0)**.

Felix Baumgartner

On a sunny Sunday morning in October 2012, sitting in a small capsule suspended from a giant helium balloon, Austrian Felix Baumgartner **(0)** ___ to a height of 24 miles (39 kilometres) above the deserts of New Mexico. Wearing a specially designed survival suit to **(1)** ___ his blood from boiling, he jumped out of the capsule and into the history books.

Baumgartner became the world's first supersonic skydiver by **(2)** ___ an estimated speed of 833 mph (1,340 kph) and breaking the sound barrier at Mach 1.24. He broke two **(3)** ___ records – the highest freefall jump and the highest balloon flight by a human – but **(4)** ___ to make the longest freefall jump, which he had also been **(5)** ___ to achieve.

A problem with his helmet nearly **(6)** ___ Baumgartner to abandon his attempt at the last minute. He was **(7)** ___ to see clearly because the heater on his visor was not working properly, causing it to fog up. **(8)** ___ , he went ahead and landed safely back on the ground just nine minutes after jumping.

0 A lifted	**B** grew	**C** rose	**D** increased
1 A avoid	**B** prevent	**C** reject	**D** deny
2 A getting	**B** arriving	**C** catching	**D** reaching
3 A added	**B** further	**C** best	**D** maximum
4 A failed	**B** missed	**C** refused	**D** disabled
5 A imagining	**B** considering	**C** hoping	**D** risking
6 A made	**B** let	**C** forced	**D** imposed
7 A incapable	**B** disallowed	**C** impractical	**D** unable
8 A Despite	**B** Although	**C** Whereas	**D** However

Formal letter

Read the following Part 2 instructions and do the related tasks in **A–C** below.

This is part of a letter from a teacher who will be staying in your area with a group of foreign students next month.

> I would be very grateful if you could provide us with information on any dance shows we could see during our stay. Is there one you would particularly recommend?
>
> Thank you in advance for your help.
>
> Yours sincerely
>
> *Ms J Appleby*

Write your **letter** in **140–190** words.

A Formal and informal style

Decide which sentence in each pair, **a** or **b**, is more formal. Tick (✓) the formal sentences. *a contraction*

1 **a** I've seen every one of their shows and I'd definitely go and see this new one if I were you.

   b I saw them on all three previous occasions and would certainly recommend going to see this latest show.

2 **a** The advert says they're strong and powerful like workmen but also really skilful tap dancers.

   b According to the publicity, the show combines the strength and power of workmen with the precision and talent of tap dancing.

formal 3 **a** Firstly, the popular Irish dance troupe 'Rhythm of the Dance' will be performing here for the fourth time in five years.

informal **b** To start with, there's the Irish dance troupe 'Rhythm of the Dance', who are on here again for the fourth time in five years.

4 **a** If you would like any further information, please do not hesitate to contact me.

   b If you want any more info, just let me know.

5 **a** I'm just writing to tell you about some of the dance shows you could go and see with your students when you come next month.

   b I am writing in reply to your request for information on dance shows which your students could see during their visit here next month.

formal 6 **a** In addition, the six Australians dance on water during the performance, splashing members of the audience in the front rows.

informal **b** Also, there's a lot of dancing on water during the show and people in the front rows get a bit wet.

7 **a** Whichever of these shows they go to, I'm sure your students will have a great time.

   b I feel certain your students would enjoy either of the shows I have described.

8 **a** There are loads of shows you could go to, but here are two I think they'll be especially interested in.

   b There is a wide range of shows to choose from, but there are two which I believe would be of particular interest to your students.

9 **a** Another option which sounds enjoyable is the all-male Australian tap dance group, 'Tap Dogs'.

   b Another one that sounds like it could be fun is 'Tap Dogs', a tap dance group from Australia with just men in it.

10 a There's the usual mix of traditional dance and music but this time apparently, they've got all the latest technology in it.

b It includes their usual mixture of traditional dance and music, but combines it, this time apparently, with up-to-date stage technology.

B A formal letter

Informal letter: pages 14–15 of the Coursebook
Put the sentences from exercise **A** in the correct order to make a letter. Write the letter in the space provided. Organize the letter into logical paragraphs.

Dear Ms Appleby

I am writing in reply to your request for information on dance shows which your students could see during their visit here next month.

_____

_____

_____

_____

_____

_____

_____

_____

_____

_____

_____

Yours sincerely

Rita Kuyper

C Writing task

Write your own answer to the question on page 18 or do the following task.

This is part of a letter from a teacher who will be staying in your area with a group of foreign students next month.

I would be very grateful if you could provide us with information on any concerts or musicals we could see during our stay. Is there one you would particularly recommend?

Thank you in advance for your help.

Yours sincerely

Mr K Simpson

Write your **letter** in 140–190 words.

③ A change for the better?

Multiple matching

1 You are going to read a magazine article in which people are interviewed about technology. Read the five texts quite quickly and decide:

a which of the people have a generally positive opinion of technology.
_____

b which of them have a more negative opinion. _____

2 For questions **1–10**, choose from the people (**A–E**). The people may be chosen more than once.

Which person

was surprised by another person's actions?	**1** ☐
often has problems with machines?	**2** ☐
finds it impossible to resist buying the latest technology?	**3** ☐
is frightened of some of the new technology?	**4** ☐
feels that technology is important in the modern-day family?	**5** ☐
does not agree with someone else in the family?	**6** ☐
has changed her way of thinking?	**7** ☐
regrets the fact that people talk less to each other face-to-face?	**8** ☐
wanted to be the same as other people?	**9** ☐
does not have much space where she lives?	**10** ☐

Technology and you

Like it or not, technology is a fact of life. But what do you think of it all? June Avery asked some of our readers.

A Angela

My elderly mother bought me a laptop recently. I couldn't believe it – like me, she's never been very keen on modern technology and there she was buying me a laptop! I live on my own in a tiny one-bedroom flat and there's not a great deal of room for anything apart from the basics. But the laptop doesn't get in the way and I can stand it up in the bookshelf when I'm not using it. I have to admit, it's very useful for storing all my recipes and I've actually grown to quite like it.

B Briony

I bought myself an e-book reader last year, partly because it **takes up** less space than a whole load of books, but also, I confess, because everyone else seemed to have one. It was a similar thing with computers, really. First I had a PC, then a laptop, followed by a netbook, a tablet … I just can't help myself. I love it all. Every time a new piece of technology **comes out**, I just have to have it, whatever it is and whether I really need it or not. And then, of course, there are smartphones. You can guarantee that if there's an overnight queue for the latest model, I'll be near the front, happy in the knowledge that it will soon be mine. I couldn't bear not to have one if I knew somebody who did.

C Carol

Our house is full of all the latest gadgets. In the kitchen alone we've got an electric carving knife, a yoghurt maker, an automatic potato peeler, a bread-making machine and a device for taking the stones out of peaches without cutting them open. As far as I'm concerned, though, they're a waste of time. They're always going wrong and my husband keeps having to mend them. I think they're more trouble than they're worth but he seems to think we couldn't **get by** without them.

D Dorothy

Like most people we have our fair share of appliances. I couldn't imagine living without a fridge freezer or a washing machine; and who hasn't got a microwave or a dishwasher nowadays? I know people had to cope without these things 50 or 60 years ago, but the world was a different place in those days, wasn't it? Things have **moved on** since then. Everything's so much faster now, and in most homes both parents go out to work. We couldn't do that *and* **bring up** children without the support of all these labour saving devices.

E Elsie

We're a bit too old for all this technology. A friend of ours says we should be on the Internet but I can't see why, and to be honest I'd be too scared to use it. It's all too fast for me. In the old days everything used to be so much simpler and people seemed to spend a lot more time chatting to each other. And by 'chatting', I mean having a proper conversation with someone who is actually physically there in front of you!

3 Match the phrasal verbs in bold in the text with the meanings **a–e**. Use the context to help you. The meanings are in the infinitive form.

   a occupy   _____

   b raise; care for a child until it is an adult _____

   c be sold to the public for the first time   _____

   d manage to survive or live   _____

   e progress or develop   _____

4 Complete the sentences with the correct form of the phrasal verbs from exercise **3**.

   1 We had to sell the car last year and we're finding it difficult to _____ without it.

   2 A new technology magazine called *Unplugged* _____ last month; they gave away a free computer game with the first copy.

   3 We're going to get a smaller table; this one _____ too much space.

   4 My parents _____ me _____ to tell the truth and I'm grateful that they did.

   5 Apparently, the world has _____ and caps no longer form part of a school uniform.

Vocabulary

Wordlist on page 206 of the Coursebook

Technology

Complete the crossword using the following clues.

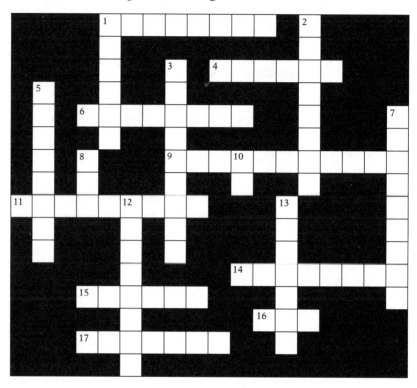

Across

1 ROFL means 'roll on the floor _____'.

4 You use a _____ control to change channels on your TV from the comfort of your sofa.

6 verb meaning 'to move information to your computer from the Internet'

9 FYI means 'for your _____'.

11 language typical in text messages, consisting of initials (e.g. 2 down), abbreviations and emoticons

14 a conventional telephone, not a mobile phone

15 verb meaning 'to look at information on the Internet'

16 In order to _____ on to a website and start using it, you may have to type your name and a password.

17 a piece of equipment worn over the ears with a part you can speak into, connected to a telephone

Down

1 a small portable computer

2 BTW stands for '_____ _____ _____'. (2, 3, 3)

3 verb meaning 'to do more than one thing at the same time', e.g. talk on a phone and work on a computer

5 adjective to describe a device which is small enough to hold in your hand

7 adjective to describe a device which can be operated without using your hands

8 The 'O' in LOL stands for '_____'.

10 preposition: ___ TV, ___ the radio, ___ the phone, ___ the Internet

12 In computing, PC stands for '_____ computer'.

13 IMO stands for 'in my _____'.

Language focus

 Grammar reference on pages 210–212 of the Coursebook

A Articles

In **1–5**, decide which gaps require an article. Write *a*, *an*, *the*, or – if no article is required.

1 _____ electric toaster was invented over _____ hundred years ago, although _____ consumers only began to show interest in it in _____ 1930s.

2 When we were on _____ holiday in _____ mountains last week we saw _____ bear.

3 She works as _____ teacher in _____ school for _____ blind in Ireland. _____ school has over _____ thousand pupils.

4 You can take _____ dogs and _____ other pets into _____ UK but they have to have either _____ EU Pet Passport or _____ Official Veterinary Health Certificate. Animals also have to have _____ microchip containing _____ information such as _____ address of the pet's owner and his/her telephone number.

5 Leslie: 'I'm looking forward to this concert. You've got _____ tickets, haven't you?'

Linda: 'Oh no! I've left them at _____ home. Don't worry, though. I'll get _____ taxi – I can be there and back in half _____ hour.'

B Comparisons

1 Complete the sentences with adjectives from the box. You may have to use the comparative or superlative form or you may not need to make any change.

boring careful cold early fast good hard hot quiet tired

1 I knew the exam would be difficult, but I didn't expect it to be as _____ as that.

2 Last summer was the _____ since records began, with temperatures reaching 40 degrees Celsius in some parts of Britain.

3 There are too many mistakes in this essay. You need to be a lot _____ .

4 He was very ill last week, but I'm pleased to say he seems to be getting _____ now.

5 They put the heating on today so the classroom wasn't quite so _____ as it was yesterday.

6 That was the _____ film I've ever seen. I almost fell asleep near the end.

7 The later you go to bed, the _____ you'll feel tomorrow.

8 We were the first guests to arrive at the party. We got there half an hour _____ than anybody else.

9 The cheetah, which can run at a speed of 110 kilometres an hour, is the _____ animal in the world.

10 Life in the countryside is so much _____ than in the city; no traffic, no crowds and no neighbours!

2 Match **1–8** to **a–h** to make logical sentences.

1 You can stay here for		**a**	as soon as he arrived.
2 I'll do my homework		**b**	as soon as you can.
3 He phoned his parents		**c**	as long as I pay for it myself.
4 Please let me know		**d**	as long as you like.
5 It was a wonderful day		**e**	as well as I can.
6 I can have a laptop		**f**	as well as a laptop.
7 She's bought a tablet		**g**	as far as that tree over there.
8 From here I can see		**h**	as far as I was concerned.

C Correcting mistakes

1 Match each paragraph **1–5** to one of the inventions from the box.

compass	radar	space blanket	video	Walkman

1 This invention <u>which</u> completely changed the lives of music-lovers around the world. At first Sony® executives thought the idea of people walking round with headphones on their heads would not be a success. But however its creator, Akio Morita, always knew that the portable device, more smaller than a paperback book, would be popular.

2 This device was the most of important navigation instrument to be invented in the last millennium. Originally, sailors used the position of the Sun and the North Star to can know which way they were going, but clouds often caused them to lose their way. This invention made possible the exploration of distant lands, including America, probably the most significant of event of civilization of the past one thousand years.

3 The first machines were built in the 1950s but for many years its cost limited its use to the television and film industry. By the early 1980s significantly very cheaper versions were introduced and became nearly as most common as television sets. It was the first device which enabled viewers to watch their favourite programmes whenever they chose and as more often as they liked.

4 This is made from a material called Mylar®, a type of the plastic covered with a microscopically thin film of metal. It is used to, for example, for exhausted marathon runners or for keeping mountaineers warm. The material existed in the 1950s but its production became much more sophisticated as a result of the man's efforts to land on the Moon in the following decade.

5 The name of this invention comes from the phrase 'radio detection and ranging' and is used for to detect the presence of objects and calculate their distance, as well as their size, shape and speed. Although originally developed as an instrument as of war, it is now used for controlling air traffic and predicting the weather. In addition to, it has important applications in astronomical research.

2 Each of the descriptions in exercise **1** has three words which should not be there. Find the words and underline them. The first one has been done for you.

Reading and Use of English

Part 2

Open cloze

For questions **1–8**, read the text below and think of the word which best fits each gap. Use only **one** word in each gap. There is an example at the beginning **(0)**. Write your answers **IN CAPITAL LETTERS**.

The negative effects of technology

Modern technology, in all **(0)** _ITS_ various forms, has changed the way we live our lives, but unfortunately, this has not always been **(1)** _____ the better. A number of things we used to value highly **(2)** _____ gradually disappearing or have disappeared altogether. Take punctuality, for example: before mobile phones, people had to keep their appointments and get to meetings **(3)** _____ time. Now, it seems, it is perfectly acceptable to send a text five minutes before you are due to meet, telling your friend or colleague **(4)** _____ to expect you for another half an hour or so.

The Internet, too, has had a negative effect on our manners. Rudeness seems to be the language of debate on any site which invites users **(5)** _____ give their opinions. Anonymity makes **(6)** _____ easier for people to insult anyone **(7)** _____ has views which are different from their own. They lose all sense of politeness and restraint, safe in the knowledge that they will never **(8)** _____ identified.

Reading and Use of English
Part 3

Word formation

For questions **1–8**, read the text below. Use the word given in capitals at the end of some of the lines to form a word that fits in the gap in the same line. There is an example at the beginning **(0)**. Write your answers **IN CAPITAL LETTERS**.

The microwave oven

One of the most **(0)** _USEFUL_ and convenient of all our	**USE**
domestic appliances is the microwave oven. Its **(1)** _____	**ABLE**
to heat and cook food fast has made it an indispensable item for	
busy people with little time to cook, and the well-equipped	
kitchen would be **(2)** _____ without one. The person	**COMPLETE**
to thank for this modern cooking miracle is **(3)** _____	**INVENT**
Percy LeBaron Spencer, who produced the 'Radarange' oven	
for industrial use in 1947. Eight years **(4)** _____ , in 1955,	**LATE**
the first domestic microwave made its **(5)** _____ . This	**APPEAR**
rather bulky contraption needed both an **(6)** _____ and a	**ELECTRIC**
plumber to install it and was the same size as a fridge. At over	
$1,000, it was not an immediate success. It wasn't until 1967,	
when the countertop model became widely available, that sales	
started to show an **(7)** _____ as the microwave grew in	**IMPROVE**
(8) _____ . It went on, of course, to become a common	**POPULAR**
feature in western homes.	

Reading and Use of English
Part 4

Transformations

For questions **1–6**, complete the second sentence so that it has a similar meaning to the first sentence, using the word given. **Do not change the word given.** You must use between **two** and **five** words, including the word given. There is an example at the beginning **(0)**. Write your answers **IN CAPITAL LETTERS**.

0 My brother isn't quite as tall as me.
SLIGHTLY
My brother is _SLIGHTLY SHORTER THAN_ me.

1 Pedro didn't use to be so thin.
THAN
Pedro is _____ be.

2 This exercise is much easier than the last one.
NEARLY
This exercise is _____ the last one.

3 My house is as big as yours.
SAME
My house _____ yours.

4 Jamie's mobile is very similar to mine.
LOT
There is not _____ Jamie's mobile phone and mine.

5 There are more boys than girls in our class.
AS
There are _____ as boys in our class.

6 I've never known anyone as clever as Hilary.
THE
Hilary is _____ ever known.

Article

1 Read the following Writing Part 2 question.

You see this notice in an international magazine.

Technology in the home
....

Technology is everywhere today, and especially in the home. We'd like you, the readers, to write a short article telling us which two modern domestic appliances or devices you would find it most difficult to live without – not forgetting, of course, to say why.

The three best articles will be published in our magazine.

Write your **article** in **140–190** words.

2 The following article was written in answer to the question in exercise **1**. Rearrange the paragraphs in the correct order, then give the article a title.

Paragraph 1 _____

Paragraph 2 _____

Paragraph 3 _____

Paragraph 4 _____

> *a   Firstly, there's the cooker, which keeps me in the kitchen for far too long. If I didn't have to cook, I could do a million and one more interesting things. But we all have to eat, and we couldn't get by on just salads and cold meat. Of course, we have a microwave, but the meals it produces just aren't as tasty as those from a conventional oven.*
>
> *b   So it's a love-hate relationship I have with these things. I hate living with them, and I can't live without them. But isn't it the same with all domestic appliances?*
>
> *c   Can you imagine an object in your house which you dislike having to use but which you know you couldn't do without? I can think of two, and just hearing their names mentioned makes me feel depressed.*
>
> *d   And perhaps worse than the cooker is the iron. The same monotonous action, forwards and backwards, hour after hour, whether it's a shirt or a skirt, shorts or trousers. No one in my family likes ironing, but anyone who wears a shirt or blouse to school or work would surely agree that sometimes the iron cannot be avoided.*

3 Look back at the article in exercise **2** and find examples of the following.

Contractions *couldn't* _____

Phrasal verbs _____

Linking words _____

Direct questions _____

4 You are going to write your own article in answer to the question in exercise **1**. Decide which two items you want to write about and plan your article using the following advice.

Title: Think of a title which will attract the reader's attention. You might like to do this when you have finished writing your article. Try to make it relevant to the whole article.

Paragraph 1: Introduction. Interest and involve your reader from the start. You could ask a direct question or make a surprising statement. You could draw attention to the similarities or differences between your two items, and/or make a general statement about how important they are to you.

Paragraph 2: Talk about your first item and why you could not live without it.

Paragraph 3: Now do the same for the second item.

Paragraph 4: Conclusion. End with a short statement or a question which summarizes your feelings and/or leaves the reader with something to think about.

5 Write your **article** in **140–190** words. Make sure you write in an appropriate style, using the features in exercise **3**.

For more help with writing articles see pages 196 and 202 of the Coursebook.

④ A good story

Multiple choice

1 You are going to read a newspaper article about a writer. For questions **1–6**, choose the answer (**A**, **B**, **C** or **D**) which you think fits best according to the article.

A writer's life: G P Taylor

J K Rowling may be responsible for the revival of fantasy fiction, but her contemporary rivals, many of whom have benefited from her success, seem reluctant to give her credit for starting a trend. Philip Pullman, for example, points out that *Northern Lights*, the first volume in his trilogy *His Dark Materials*, was published a year before Harry Potter's adventures began. So it comes as a surprise when G P Taylor concedes that he only wrote a novel because of the enormous popularity of Harry Potter.

Taylor is the Yorkshire vicar who sold his motorbike to self-publish 2,000 copies of his first novel, *Shadowmancer*, a book that was subsequently picked up by publishers Faber & Faber and got to number one in the *New York Times* bestseller list. His novels conjure up dark, **chilling** worlds in which the supernatural threatens to take over, yet he describes his life as a writer in flatly functional terms. For example, he is able to name the exact day that he became a novelist: March 21, 2002. 'It was one of those **seminal** moments in my life. Harry Potter was becoming very popular. And I thought, "This woman's written a book. I might write one." '

'I got a copy of Harry Potter, counted the number of words that were on the page, measured the width of the margin, counted the number of chapters in the book, how many pages were in the book and set my computer screen up so that it would have 468 words on the page. My chapters were the same length as the Harry Potter chapters; I thought, "This must be how you write a book." '

Shadowmancer is a simple and uncomplicated fantasy – and Taylor, who is his own most effective critic, makes few further claims for the novel. 'It's a great story, but if I'd written it now, it would be a completely different book. In many ways, it's a **clumsy** classic. There are a lot of things in there that I would get rid of. And yet, I think that's the big attraction. It's because it's an incredible adventure story, written by a non-writer, just a storyteller.'

Taylor returns to this distinction between writing and storytelling a number of times, distancing himself from grand and **lofty** ideas of the novelist's purpose. He describes himself as a 'fairly uneducated, council-house kid' who ran away to London as a teenager, 'a bit of a chancer, with ideas above his station'. He read Dickens, lots of Orwell – 'they were **trendy** books to read' – and Kerouac. But he is uncomfortable talking at any length about favourite novels or influences beyond Rowling: 'I have not read all that many books. I'm not, you know, a very **literate** person.'

Taylor was a rock-music promoter in his twenties and remains a showman, happiest in front of a crowd. He describes the talks he gives in schools and at book festivals, dressed up as a sea captain or as an 18th-century highwayman in a long black coat. 'You're using your face, you're using your body, you're acting out what you're doing.' The business of putting his thoughts in writing can be problematic in comparison. As a storyteller, in order to demonstrate shock or alarm to an audience he will 'pause between sentences and show a wide-eyed, staring face. But to describe that in English …' Taylor breaks off and begins an imaginary dictation. 'Then he stopped. There was a long silence. Da da da da da da.' He laughs. 'Well, I can get that effect in a second by breathing in deeply.'

It is unusual to hear a writer speak in such a **dismissive** way of his craft. 'Movies excite more people than books,' he explains. 'We're living in a visual age and I think, as we go on, books will have lesser importance.'

1 The writer says that many fantasy fiction writers would not agree that
   A they have copied their ideas from J K Rowling.
   B J K Rowling's success has contributed to their own.
   C fantasy fiction will remain fashionable for many years.
   D J K Rowling is a writer of fantasy fiction in the true sense.

2 The writer is surprised by
   A the success of Taylor's books.
   B the short time Taylor has been a writer.
   C the number of books Taylor has published.
   D Taylor's honesty about why he wrote his first book.

3 What aspect of the Harry Potter books does Taylor admit to imitating?
   A the writing style
   B the storylines
   C the layout
   D the cover design

4 What does Taylor say about *Shadowmancer*?
   A He is aware of its limitations.
   B He did not write all of it himself.
   C He is going to write a revised edition.
   D It does not deserve the praise it receives.

5 What opinion does Taylor have of himself?
   A He is very proud of his achievements as a writer.
   B He thinks he is a better writer than J K Rowling.
   C He does not regard himself as a serious novelist.
   D He feels he deserves greater recognition.

6 What do we learn about the talks Taylor gives?
   A He enjoys them more than being a promoter.
   B He couldn't do them without dressing up.
   C He finds them easier than writing.
   D He likes shocking people.

2 Match the words in bold in the text with the meanings **a–g**. Use the context to help you.
   a important and having a great influence   _____
   b showing you think something is not important _____
   c frightening   _____
   d careless and unskilful   _____
   e intelligent and well-educated   _____
   f modern and fashionable   _____
   g noble and important   _____

Vocabulary

Wordlist on pages 206–207 of the Coursebook

A Cinema and films

Use the clues below to complete the grid. When you have all the answers you will find an extra word for number 11 down.

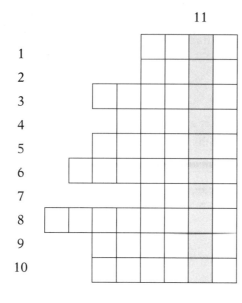

1 the people who act in a film

2 the story of a film

3 actors wear this, sometimes changing their appearance completely

4 a part of a film in which the action occurs in one place at one time, e.g. a love _____ , an action _____

5 a film which is intended to make you laugh

6 special _____ are unusual images or sounds created by using special techniques

7 another word for 'role'

8 a man who performs a dangerous piece of action in a film instead of the actor

9 a box _____ hit is a film which is very successful

10 a film that has a similar story and title to a film made earlier

B Expressions with *take*

Lexical phrase list on page 133

Complete the sentences with appropriate words from the box. In **1–6**, pay special attention to the prepositions in bold.

> advice   blame   care   courage   interest   joke   notice   offence   pity   risk

1 He takes a very keen _____ **in** music and often goes to concerts.

2 Don't say anything negative about her hair; she's very sensitive and might take _____ **at** your remarks.

3 When I got on the bus I realized I didn't have any money. But as it was snowing heavily, the driver took _____ **on** me and let me stay on without paying.

4 If a team loses, it's normally the manager who takes the _____ **for** the defeat and not the players.

5 Our neighbour has agreed to take _____ **of** the dogs while we're on holiday.

6 The doctor told her to eat less, but she didn't take any _____ **of** him. She still eats far too much.

7 Although she really wanted to study Archaeology, she took her parents' _____ and went to Law school.

8 Jamie likes making fun of other people but he can't take a _____ himself. He gets so angry.

9 It took a lot of _____ to ride his motorbike again after the accident.

10 She was taking a big _____ when she changed career, but fortunately everything went well and she really likes her new job.

C Phrasal verbs with *take*

Phrasal verb list on pages 130–132
Complete the sentences with an appropriate particle.

1 Our maths teacher, Mrs Hill, is going to have a baby so Mr Bennett is taking _____ until she comes back.
2 I'd love to take _____ golf, but it's such an expensive sport.
3 We haven't really taken _____ the new boss; he's a little too formal for us.
4 She takes _____ her father; they're both as disorganized as each other.
5 They've taken _____ another receptionist at work; Jo couldn't manage on her own.
6 Before play continued, the referee took the player _____ and told him to calm down.

D Word formation: Adjectives ending in *-ing* and *-ed*

Use the word given in capitals at the end of some of the lines to form a word that fits in the space in the same line. The word you require may be an adjective or an adverb. It might be positive or negative.

1 *The Shining* is probably the most _____ film I've ever seen. **FRIGHT**
2 I get so _____ when my dad starts singing. **EMBARRASS**
3 As exam day approached, Ian became _____ nervous. **INCREASE**
4 **A**: I think I'll go straight to bed. It was a very _____ journey. **TIRE**
  B: Yes, you must be _____ . **EXHAUST**
5 I didn't really enjoy the film. The special effects were OK but the plot was rather dull and _____ . **INTEREST**
6 Johnny Depp is not one of my favourite actors but he gave a _____ good performance in this film. **SURPRISE**
7 You look a little _____ . Don't you understand what you have to do in this exercise? **CONFUSE**
8 It was quite _____ to read so many negative reviews of **ANNOY**
  the film. Critics wrote that the main characters were _____ , **CONVINCE**
  but personally, I was very _____ by the quality of the **IMPRESS**
  acting and would certainly recommend the film to other people.

Language focus

Grammar reference on page 212 of the Coursebook

A Tenses

1 Complete the sentences with an appropriate past tense form of the verb in brackets. Choose from the past simple, past continuous, past perfect simple and past perfect continuous.

1 Susana _____ (live) in Germany for only three weeks when she _____ (start) going out with Reiner. At that time he _____ (train) to be a teacher. She _____ (meet) him at a college disco.
2 When I _____ (hear) about the motorway accident on the radio, I immediately _____ (phone) my son to check that he _____ (get) back safely. He _____ (tell) me he _____ (take) a different route home.
3 We _____ (watch) a particularly romantic scene in a film at the cinema when my boyfriend's mobile phone _____ (go) off. He _____ (forget) to switch it off.
4 By the time we _____ (get) to the party they _____ (eat) all the food. In fact, it was so late that most of the guests _____ (already/leave) and only two or three people _____ (still/dance).

2 Complete the story with an appropriate past tense form of verbs from the box.

> agree carry fly happen have land pick progress put see talk work

On 'parents' evenings' teachers speak to parents about how well their children are doing at school. Last parents' evening my mum **(1)** _____ away from home, and my dad, who **(2)** _____ a minor operation the day before, had to stay at home and rest. So my grandmother **(3)** _____ to go to it with me and talk to my teachers about how I **(4)** _____ . While we **(5)** _____ to my maths teacher, my gran suddenly coughed and her false teeth **(6)** _____ out of her mouth and **(7)** _____ on the desk in front of my teacher. My teacher tried to pretend she **(8)** _____ not _____ anything, by appearing to be looking for something in her bag. But my gran just **(9)** _____ up her teeth, **(10)** _____ them back in her mouth and **(11)** _____ on talking as if nothing **(12)** _____ .

B Linking words

In **1–5**, underline the most suitable linking word or expression.

1 Last summer we stayed in an apartment near the beach *during/for/in* three weeks.

2 *As/During/Whereas* I was walking to school this morning, I found a £1 coin.

3 I looked everywhere for my hat. *In the end/At the end/At last* I had to buy a new one.

4 You're here *by the time/at the end/at last*! Where have you been? We were worried.

5 *Afterwards/After/After that* she'd taken the dog for a walk, she made a cup of tea.

Reading and Use of English
Part 4

Transformations

For questions **1–6**, complete the second sentence so that it has a similar meaning to the first sentence, using the word given. Do not change the word given. You must use between **two** and **five** words, including the word given. Write your answers **IN CAPITAL LETTERS**.

1 I enjoyed myself so much I didn't want to come home.

GOOD

I had _____ time I didn't want to come home.

2 It was such an interesting book that I stayed up all night to finish it.

SO

I was _____ that I stayed up all night to finish it.

3 How long is the car journey from London to Manchester?

TAKE

How long _____ drive by car from London to Manchester?

4 Eleanor is clearly proud of her achievements.

PRIDE

Eleanor clearly _____ her achievements.

5 We will phone you the moment we get to the hotel.

ARRIVE

We will phone you as _____ the hotel.

6 I finished my library book and returned it when the lesson finished.

END

I finished my library book and took _____ of the lesson.

Reading and Use of English
Part 1

Multiple-choice cloze

For questions **1–8**, read the text below and decide which answer (**A**, **B**, **C** or **D**) best fits each gap. There is an example at the beginning (**0**).

The Academy Awards

The first Academy Awards ceremony was (**0**) ___ on 16 May 1929 over dinner in Hollywood's Roosevelt Hotel. It was (**1**) ___ by 270 people, each paying $5 to bring a guest, and hosted by silent-movie actor Douglas Fairbanks, who (**2**) ___ out the awards in a few minutes. The 12 winners had been (**3**) ___ three months beforehand and the very first 'Oscar®' – a 34cm-tall gold-plated statuette designed by MGM's art director, Cedric Gibbons – had already been handed to German actor Emil Jannings, who had sailed to Europe a few weeks before. Actually, Jannings was the (**4**) ___ in the Best Actor category, the real winner being Rin Tin Tin, a celebrity dog, but the new awards ceremony wanted to be (**5**) ___ seriously.

(**6**) ___ to legend, a librarian in the offices of the Academy of Motion Picture Arts and Sciences, which awards the prizes, saw a statuette and said: 'Gee! He looks just (**7**) ___ my Uncle Oscar.' The name stuck, and so did the 'Little Man', who remains the single most prized object in the (**8**) ___ multi-billion-dollar movie business.

0	**A** placed	**B** dated	**C** called	**D** held
1	**A** participated	**B** assisted	**C** attended	**D** presented
2	**A** put	**B** turned	**C** gave	**D** let
3	**A** revealed	**B** advertised	**C** said	**D** averted
4	**A** bystander	**B** onlooker	**C** passer-by	**D** runner-up
5	**A** looked	**B** had	**C** made	**D** taken
6	**A** Due	**B** Owing	**C** According	**D** Thanks
7	**A** so	**B** like	**C** how	**D** as
8	**A** entire	**B** full	**C** wide	**D** all

Reading and Use of English
Part 2

Open cloze

For questions **1–8**, read the text below and think of the word which best fits each gap. Use only **one** word in each gap. There is an example at the beginning (**0**). Write your answers **IN CAPITAL LETTERS**.

Doing it again

A friend once boasted to me that she (**0**) _HAD_ seen the film *The Sound of Music* no fewer (**1**) _____ 17 times. Personally, I cannot imagine (**2**) _____ greater waste of one's time (once was enough for me), but I have to confess (**3**) _____ are films I, too, have watched on multiple occasions (**4**) _____ ever growing tired of them. Indeed, some films have benefited from a second viewing, in exactly the (**5**) _____ way that one's enjoyment of a novel can improve on the second, third or fourth reading. It often feels like a different experience.

And a recent study (**6**) _____ shown that it actually is different; that rereading books, watching films again, or revisiting places where you have been happy, results (**7**) _____ a 'new or renewed appreciation' of the experience. The study says that doing something again enables people not only to relive the past experience, (**8**) _____ also to discover new details. 'Therefore, the experience is different, even though it is repeated,' the research concludes. 'By doing it again, people get more out of it.'

Writing
Part 1

Essay

1 a Read the following Part 1 instructions.

In your English class you have been talking about films and books. Your English teacher has asked you to write an essay.

Write an essay using **all** the notes and give reasons for your point of view.

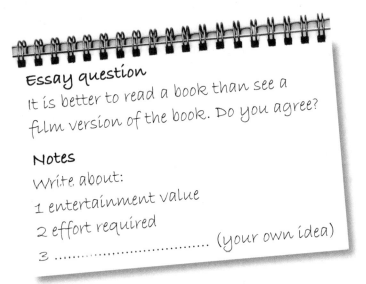

Essay question
It is better to read a book than see a
film version of the book. Do you agree?

Notes
Write about:
1 entertainment value
2 effort required
3 .... (your own idea)

Write your **essay** in **140–190** words.

b Read the following answer to the task in **a** and answer the questions 1 and 2.

1 What is the purpose of each paragraph?

Paragraph 1: Introduction: general statement

2 What point does the writer make for 'your own idea' (number 3 in the Notes section in **a**)?

Many of people prefer watching a film to reading the same story in a book. Both forms of entertainment have their advantages and disadvantages.

In the one hand, books offer more entertainment value than films. It takes more time to read a book, so the enjoyment lasts more longer. In addition, readers can use their imagination to decide what do the characters and places in the story look like, whereas the film gives only one interpretation, which might not be the best. Furthermore, the most interested scenes in the book may be cut for the film, sometimes with a negative effect on the story.

On the other hand, watching a film takes less effort that reading a novel, which requires more active participation from the reader. Consequently, the film version is ideal if you are too tired to open book. A further advantage of films is that they are very visual and often, therefore, more memorable. You may need reading a book more than once to fix it in your memory.

On balance, I think always it is better to read the story first. Afterwards you can see it on film if you want compare.

2 a Read the examiner's comments on the essay on page 34, then follow the instructions in **b**.

> <u>Strong points</u>
> This is clearly a well-organized answer. The ideas are grouped logically into paragraphs and a number of linking words have been used to connect the different points. The essay is written in an appropriately formal style and there is a good range of vocabulary and structures.
>
> <u>Weak points</u>
> There are a number of grammatical errors throughout the essay, though these do not prevent understanding.

b There are ten grammatical mistakes in the essay. Correct the mistakes, paying particular attention to the following areas of grammar:

- use of gerund and infinitive
- comparative forms
- position of frequency adverbs
- use of articles
- adjectives ending in *-ing/-ed*
- prepositions

3 a Read the following Part 1 question. Read the advice in **b** before you write your answer.

You have recently had a discussion in your English class comparing watching films at home and at the cinema. Now, your teacher has asked you to write an essay.

Write an essay using **all** the notes and give reasons for your point of view.

Write your essay in **140–190** words.

b Before you write your answer, make sure you plan what you are going to say.

- Decide what 'your own idea' will be for the third point in the Notes section. Here are some possibilities:

  which is cheaper

  which offers better quality viewing

  which is more enjoyable to do with friends or family

- Write a paragraph plan. You may use one of the examples below, or any other plan which enables you to organize your ideas logically.

Essay question
It is better to watch a film at home rather than in a cinema. Do you agree?

Notes
Write about:
1 which is more comfortable
2 which has a better atmosphere
3 .... (your own idea)

n't forget!

onnect your ideas ing linking devices. ge 39 of Unit 3 in e Coursebook has a ection of these. eck your work for stakes when you ve written your essay. e the checklist in **2b** ove.

Plan A
(Paragraphs 2 and 3 could be written as three paragraphs.)
Paragraph 1: General statement: both have their advantages
Paragraph 2: Advantages of watching a film at home: more comfortable and cheaper
Paragraph 3: Advantage of watching a film in a cinema: better atmosphere
Paragraph 4: Conclusion: state your opinion

Plan B
(Paragraphs 2–4 could be written as two paragraphs.)
Paragraph 1: General statement, giving opinion: better in a cinema
Paragraph 2: Why watching a film in a cinema is more comfortable
Paragraph 3: Why it is more enjoyable to watch a film with friends in a cinema
Paragraph 4: Why the atmosphere in a cinema is better for watching a film
Paragraph 5: Conclusion: restate your opinion

Multiple matching

1 You are going to read an article about the job of an air traffic controller. For questions **1–10**, choose from the paragraphs (**A–E**). The paragraphs may be chosen more than once.

Which paragraph mentions the following?

the need for perseverance	1
activity during rest periods	2
a common misconception	3
the importance of being able to work with others	4
the advantage of the predictability in the working hours	5
variety within the same job	6
the writer's previous experience in a related field	7
informing others of changes	8
the need for concentration	9
receiving individual on-the-job guidance	10

Air traffic controllers

Sonia Avogadro is an area controller at the London Terminal Control Centre, West Drayton, which controls air space in south-east England.

A My job is about giving instructions and any other relevant information to aircraft, so they can fly as quickly and safely as possible. I work on air traffic flying into Gatwick, organizing the planes into a neat sequence so they all come in one after another. I'm in constant radio contact with the pilots, keeping them up-to-date on the weather and any unusual conditions or alterations in flight plans. The main thing I need to monitor is the level or altitude I want them to fly at. A lot of people think air-traffic controllers work in a control tower, but in fact, only 20 per cent do. They're the ones who deal with take-offs and landings. Most of us work at area control centres away from the airport.

B I work in shifts on radar for up to two hours, then I always have a half-hour break, where I'll move around and give my eyes a good rub. The breaks are for safety purposes. I suppose that working shifts might not suit everybody. Because it's a 24-hour business, there's a lot of getting up early and night shifts. We work a repetitive roster – two mornings, two afternoons, then two nights – so there are six night-shifts a month. The good thing is that the shift pattern is always the same, so at least you can plan your life around it.

C It's a job that means something – you're looking after people's safety, so there's a real consequence to what you do. I really like the fact that it's always different. You

might be working with completely different people, traffic and weather conditions every day. And at the end of your shift, you take your headset off and that's it. You don't have to take the job home with you.

D You've got to be the sort of person who can really focus on the task in hand, and process large amounts of complex data. Because very complicated air traffic situations can happen extremely quickly, you've got to be calm, stay on the ball, and react very quickly. You also need excellent spatial awareness. And a key quality in the job is the need to be a good team player, someone who can get on with a lot of different people.

E I was an air hostess for a while after university, so I've seen the other side of the business. One day I went up to the control tower for a visit, and thought the job looked fascinating. So I applied, and luckily I got a place to train. You have to spend up to 12 months at a college of air-traffic control, using super hi-tech computer simulators.

Once you graduate from the college, you get posted to a unit where you do more practical training, with the help of a mentor, for six months to two years. And when that's finished, you have to sit a final exam. I'd say that if you decide to apply, stick with it and be prepared for some very tough training. It's not a walk in the park, but it's very rewarding once you get through it.

The words for some people and machines can be formed by adding the suffixes *-er* or *-or* to the verb. Note how in these examples from the text, spelling changes are also sometimes required.

Verb	Person or machine	Spelling changes
control	controller	add an extra *l*
play	player	no spelling change
compute	computer	add only *r* to the verb
simulate	simulator	remove *e* at the end of the verb, add *-or*

2 Make spelling changes to the verbs **1–10** to make the name of a person or a machine.

Verb	Person or machine
0 read	*reader*
1 scan	_____
2 calculate	_____
3 advise	_____
4 invent	_____
5 present	_____
6 demonstrate	_____
7 compete	_____
8 photocopy	_____
9 research	_____
10 spectate	_____

Vocabulary

Wordlist on page 207 of the Coursebook

A Jobs

Complete the crossword using the following clues.

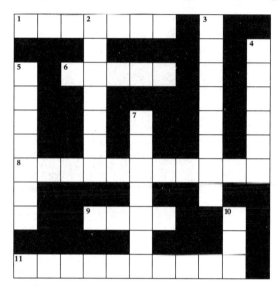

Across

This person …

1 takes away people's rubbish.
6 makes and sells bread and cakes.
8 cuts people's hair.
9 cooks in a restaurant or hotel.
11 looks after the financial matters of a person or company.

Down

This person …

2 helps you to pass the *Cambridge English: First* exam.
3 serves people with food and drink in a restaurant.
4 gives advice to people about law and represents them in court.
5 cuts up and sells meat.
7 operates on people.
10 treats sick or injured animals.

B Questions and answers

1 Match the questions **1–8** to the answers **a–h**.

1 Do you have a well-paid job?
2 Do you find it challenging?
3 Is it a satisfying job?
4 Do you have to be fair?
5 Is fitness a requirement?
6 Do you need artistic skills?
7 Have you ever been on strike?
8 Will you retire when you're 65?

a Yes, it is; it gives me a lot of pleasure.
b No, I have nothing to complain about.
c Yes, I have to treat everyone equally.
d No, I'll probably go on working.
e Yes, I earn a good living.
f No, physical strength isn't necessary.
g Yes, I do; it really tests my abilities.
h No, it's not a particularly creative job.

2 What job might the person being interviewed in exercise **1** have? Choose from the words in the box. More than one answer may be possible.

accountant	architect	civil servant	company director	cook
firefighter	judge	police officer	politician	surgeon

C Expressions with *work*

Complete the sentences with the correct form of the verb *work* in the first gap and a word or expression from the box in the second gap.

| flexitime | for myself | full-time | long hours | overtime | part-time |

1 I _____ ten hours' _____ last week and earned £300 on top of my salary.

2 You should be prepared _____ _____ as an accountant; eight in the morning till eight in the evening is not uncommon.

3 I'm _____ _____ at the moment; four hours instead of the normal eight. I'll go back to _____ _____ when John's old enough to go to school.

4 I'd quite like _____ _____ ; if you oversleep, your boss doesn't get angry, and if you want to leave work early, you can.

5 I've always _____ _____ ; I couldn't imagine not being my own boss.

D Confusing words

Underline the correct alternative.

1 Was Jim asked to leave the company or was it his own decision to *sack/resign*?

2 I enjoy my job but I don't *earn/win* very much – I think I should be paid more.

3 Jim's got his own taxi business now – he *ran/set* it up a year ago with his son.

4 Are you going to *apply/demand* for that job you saw advertised in the newspaper?

5 Elisa got a university *career/degree* in Geography, but now she can't find a job.

Language focus

 Grammar reference on pages 213–214 of the Coursebook

A Noun phrases

Underline the correct alternative.

1 I read an article about corruption in last *Sunday/Sunday's* newspaper.

2 Noel said he'd wait for me at the *bottom of the stairs/stairs' bottom*.

3 I've just *drunk/broken* a milk bottle.

4 The *post man/postman* is coming through the *garden gate/gardengate*.

5 'What's that brown stain on the sofa?' 'I spilt a *coffee cup/cup of coffee* on it.'

6 Maria suffers from a *lack of confidence/confidence lack*.

7 The neighbours have just come back from a *month/month's* holiday.

8 I bought this in the *January/January's* sales. Do you like it?

B Obligation, necessity and permission

1 Complete the sentences with verbs from the box. Do not change the form of the verbs. There are four extra verbs you do not need to use.

| allow | allowed | don't have | had | have | let | made |
| make | must | mustn't | ought | should | shouldn't | would |

1 You _____ stay at home if you're feeling ill. That's my advice, anyway.

2 My parents won't _____ me go horse-riding – they think it's too dangerous.

3 You _____ talk at all during the exam, and you aren't _____ to use a mobile phone. Anyone breaking these rules will _____ to leave the room immediately.

4 You _____ really eat so much chocolate – it's not good for you.

5 I _____ to do what you tell me – you can't _____ me clean up the mess!

6 You really _____ to try to stop biting your nails. They look so ugly like that.

7 You _____ better hurry up or you'll be late!

2 Complete the sentences with a pair of words from the box.

| can/can't | ~~can/must~~ | can/should | can't/must | needn't/must | shouldn't/must |

0 A: Is it OK if I go to London with my friends at the weekend, Mum?

  B: You ___can___ go if you want to, but you ___must___ phone me when you get there.

1 A: Are you sure it's OK to come in here?

  B: Well, we _____ really be here, but I _____ just show you this.

2 A: Could I borrow an atlas?

  B: Well, you _____ certainly have a look at it here, but you _____ take it home with you, I'm afraid.

3 A: Do I have to write the date on this piece of work?

  B: No, you _____ write the date, but you _____ remember to put your name.

4 A: Could I take the dog for a walk?

  B: Yes, of course you _____ , but I think you _____ wear your boots, don't you? It's very wet outside.

5 A: My parents won't let me go and see that film.

  B: Well, if you _____ see it now, you _____ try and see it when you're older.

Multiple-choice cloze

For questions **1–8**, read the text below and decide which answer (**A**, **B**, **C** or **D**) best fits each gap. There is an example at the beginning (**0**).

Striking Mom

Canadian mother Jessica Stilwell became an internet hit after (**0**) ____ on strike for six days, refusing to tidy up after her three daughters, and (**1**) ____ a blog called *Striking Mom* which documented the chaos that followed. Sitting down one day (**2**) ____ the mess left by her three daughters, she decided enough was enough. The normally houseproud Mrs Stilwell (**3**) ____ that she would be doing no more tidying, cleaning or picking up after the children.

Mrs Stilwell did not tell her daughters about her 'experiment', in order to see how long it would (**4**) ____ for them to begin cleaning up after themselves. On day four, one daughter told Mrs Stilwell a (**5**) ____ of seventeen times that the kitchen was disgusting, but still did nothing about it. Mrs Stilwell said: 'Each one (**6**) ____ the others for the mess and they began yelling at one (**7**) ____ .' By day six the girls eventually gave in, with one of them breaking (**8**) ____ and begging for help to clean up.

0	**A** gaining	**B** getting	**C** <u>going</u>	**D** giving
1	**A** setting up	**B** handing over	**C** taking in	**D** getting by
2	**A** throughout	**B** between	**C** aside	**D** among
3	**A** declared	**B** notified	**C** talked	**D** spoke
4	**A** last	**B** take	**C** spend	**D** endure
5	**A** figure	**B** sum	**C** total	**D** whole
6	**A** accused	**B** charged	**C** blamed	**D** faulted
7	**A** selves	**B** another	**C** together	**D** own
8	**A** in	**B** out	**C** up	**D** down

Open cloze

For questions **1–8**, read the text below and think of the word which best fits each gap. Use only **one** word in each gap. There is an example at the beginning **(0)**. Write your answers **IN CAPITAL LETTERS**.

A new life

I used to work **(0)** ___*AS*___ an accountant in a large furniture factory in London. I had a responsible job and was earning **(1)** _____ good living until the company started having problems. Eventually, I was **(2)** _____ redundant.

My husband and I had always wanted to go **(3)** _____ business together, and we both felt that now was a good time to take a risk and do **(4)** _____ different. Jonathan, my husband, gave **(5)** _____ his well-paid but stressful job in the City and we bought a pub in a village near York.

It took **(6)** _____ both quite a long time to get used to living in the countryside. Everything happens at a much slower pace here, but the people are friendlier than in London and we couldn't imagine going back **(7)** _____ to live. We still work as hard **(8)** _____ we did before, but it's so much more satisfying working for yourself.

Word formation

For questions **1–8**, read the text below. Use the word given in capitals at the end of some of the lines to form a word that fits in the gap in the same line. There is an example at the beginning **(0)**. Write your answers **IN CAPITAL LETTERS**.

Don't forget!

You may need to use the negative form of an adjective or adverb.

A driving instructor

Susan Bird has been a driving **(0)** _INSTRUCTOR_ in London for	**INSTRUCT**
twenty years. 'You need a great deal of **(1)** _____ to do	**PATIENT**
this job,' she explains, 'and the **(2)** _____ to repeat	**ABLE**
things several times without getting **(3)** _____ .' Susan	**ANNOY**
says she generally finds that women are better students then men.	
'Although they are often accused of being bad drivers, women tend to	
drive more carefully than men and don't mind being told what to do.	
Men, on the other hand, have more **(4)** _____ , but aren't	**CONFIDENT**
very good listeners.' She talks about the reactions of other road users	
to learner drivers. 'On the whole, other drivers understand what it's	
like to be a learner and are very considerate. **(5)** _____ ,	**FORTUNATE**
however, some can be very intolerant; there are times when I have been	
shouted at and even **(6)** _____ by drivers who haven't	**THREAT**
been able to overtake.' But her face suddenly **(7)** _____	**BRIGHT**
when she is asked whether she enjoys her work. 'Yes, of course!' she	
exclaims. 'It's an extremely **(8)** _____ job, particularly	**SATISFY**
when your students pass!'	

Transformations

For questions **1–6**, complete the second sentence so that it has a similar meaning to the first sentence, using the word given. Do not change the word given. You must use between **two** and **five** words, including the word given. Write your answers **IN CAPITAL LETTERS**.

1 The sign says that cigarettes must be extinguished.

  HAVE

  According to the sign, _____ out your cigarette.

2 What's their expected time of arrival?

  SUPPOSED

  What time _____ arrive?

3 I don't think you should drink any more coffee.

  BETTER

  You _____ any more coffee.

4 You shouldn't be so impatient.

  OUGHT

  You _____ patience.

5 I'm not allowed to stay out later than 10 o'clock.

  LET

  My parents _____ out later than 10 o'clock.

6 The science teacher made me clean all the test tubes.

  MADE

  I _____ all the test tubes by the science teacher.

Letter of application

1 Read the following Part 2 instructions.

You see the following advertisement in your local English-language newspaper.

> **Summer holiday job opportunity**
>
> I am looking for a friendly young person to look after my elderly mother during the summer holiday period. You would be expected to do some housework and cook. Personal qualities are just as important as experience and a reasonable knowledge of English is essential.
>
> Please write to me, Mrs Adams, saying why you think you would be suitable for the job.

Write your **letter of application** in **140–190** words.

2 Sentences **a–j** are from a letter which was written in reply to the advertisement in exercise **1**. Put them in the correct order and arrange them into paragraphs. Complete the paragraph plan below.

1 Reason for writing _____

2 Personal details and qualities _____

3 Experience _____

4 Relevant skills _____

5 Closing comments _____

> Dear Mrs Adams,
>
> **a** As well as being honest and reliable, I am always cheerful and can keep smiling in any situation.
>
> **b** I am 18 years old and I will be starting university in September.
>
> **c** In return, my grandmother has taught me to cook and thanks to her, I have become quite skilled in the kitchen.
>
> **d** I also have a great deal of patience, particularly when dealing with other people.
>
> **e** I hope you will consider my application and I look forward to receiving your reply.
>
> **f** I know I would enjoy helping your mother and I feel I have the necessary qualities for this job.
>
> **g** I am writing to apply for the job you advertised in last month's issue of 'English Weekly'.
>
> **h** Apart from my personal qualities, I have experience of looking after my own grandmother, who lives here at home with us.
>
> **i** Finally, I also have a reasonable level of English and am about to take the Cambridge English: First Certificate examination.
>
> **j** I help to wash her, go out for short walks with her and occasionally read to her.
>
> Yours sincerely
>
> Dalia Vaivadaite

3 Underline the correct alternative to explain how to end a letter.

   a When we give the name of the person we are writing to at the beginning of the letter (e.g. 'Dear Mrs Adams'), we put 'Yours *faithfully/sincerely*' at the end.

   b When we write 'Dear Sir or Madam' at the beginning of the letter, we put 'Yours *faithfully/sincerely*' at the end.

4 Write an answer to the following Part 2 task, using the paragraph plan and accompanying comments and questions to help you. You should write between **140** and **190** words.

You see this advertisement in an English newspaper.

fore you write

ad the information
out Letters of
plication on pages
–21 of the Coursebook.

> We are looking for a lively young person to look after our two children (aged eight and six) during the summer holidays. Applicants should enjoy being with children and be capable of keeping them occupied and entertained both inside and outside of the house.
>
> Please write to Mr and Mrs Jackson, saying why you think you would be suitable for the job.

Write your **letter of application**.

Paragraph plan

1 Reason for writing

In which issue of which newspaper did you see the advertisement?

2 Personal details and qualities

- Mention your age and say what you do.
- Why are you interested in the job?
- What qualities do you have which might be appropriate?

3 Experience

What experience do you have of being with children?

4 Relevant interests and skills

What interests and skills do you have which might be useful for this job?
Remember, you can invent information!

5 Closing comments

End in an appropriate way. Will you write *Yours sincerely* or *Yours faithfully*?

Gapped text

1 You are going to read an article about Sydney Chaplin, the brother of the silent film star, Charlie. Six sentences have been removed from the article. Choose from the sentences **A–G** the one which fits each gap **(1–6)**. There is one extra sentence which you do not need to use.

THE OTHER CHAPLIN

This is the story of a man named Chaplin, who extracted himself from poverty with the discovery that he could make people laugh, first in British music halls and later in Hollywood. By the early 1920s, he was shooting big-budget features on a million-dollar contract. But this man's name was not Charlie.

In the early 20th century, there was room in the world for two Chaplins. Their names appeared together in print on the pages of fan magazines, and side by side in ink on the document that founded United Artists. **1** Even among silent-film specialists, his work is not well known.

Mention his name to any of Charlie's older children, however, and their faces light up with pleasure. 'Uncle Sydney was our favourite!' Geraldine Chaplin told me. Michael, Charlie's eldest son, can still conjure the distinctive smell of his cigars. Geraldine can remember the traces of a London accent in his voice. **2** 'He loved to drive his great big Cadillac along the narrow Swiss roads,' Geraldine told me. 'He'd drive very, very slowly – it took him about an hour to get from Lausanne – and other cars would be honking around him.'

Best of all, they remember the good-natured anarchy which he brought to Vevey, their childhood home in Switzerland. 'As a kid,' Michael said, 'it was a relief to see him. **3** He was always clowning about – in contrast to my father, who, to me, was always a more severe man, always on my back about working hard at school and getting a good education.'

Sydney Chaplin was born in 1885, the first son of a seamstress named Hannah Hill. 'It seems strange to me,' reflected Hannah's sister, Kate Mowbray, in 1916, 'that anyone can write about Charlie Chaplin without mentioning his brother Sydney. **4** Syd, of quiet manner, clever brain and steady nerve, has been father and mother to Charlie. Charlie has always looked up to Syd, and Sydney would suffer anything to spare Charlie.'

5 Sydney had become a leading member of Fred Karno's gang of acrobatic comedians, touring the States on a weekly salary of $36. In 1908, he persuaded Karno to admit his brother to the company on a trial basis. Karno sent Charlie to do the next American tour, in the autumn of 1910. Before long, Charlie had accepted a contract with Mack Sennett's Keystone Pictures in Edendale, California. Not forgetting that one good turn deserves another, he persuaded Sennett that Sydney would make a useful addition. By November 1914, the Little Tramp had been joined by Sydney's most famous character, Gussle – a buffoon with a cane, tiny fedora hat and big moustache.

Throughout his life, Sydney put his own performing career on hold to manage Charlie's affairs. He negotiated his brother's first million-dollar contract in 1917; represented him in the foundation of United Artists in 1919; and quashed reports in 1931 about Charlie's affair with a woman named May Reeves by pretending that he had enjoyed an affair with her himself. 'They had a very close relationship,' Michael told me. 'My father didn't have that many friends. **6** But he never said anything derogatory about Sydney. They really loved each other.'

A This observation was never more true than in their twenties and thirties, when they were building their careers as comedians.

B And both recall his cautious attitude to motoring.

C They have been inseparable all their lives.

D His failure to take anything seriously created tensions.

E Yet while Charlie remains famous the world over, the memory of his brother has largely been forgotten.

F He would always joke and play magic tricks, make coins disappear, fall off a chair.

G He was a hard man to get along with.

Homographs are words which have the same spelling but different meanings. They may also be pronounced in different ways.

*They had a very **close** relationship.*	/kləʊs/ = strong
*I'll **close** the window – it's cold in here.*	/kləʊz/ = shut

---

2 Complete sentence **b** with a homograph from sentence **a**. Decide if the two words have the same or a different pronunciation. Write **S** for the same and **D** for different.

0 a Their names appeared together in print on the pages of fan magazines.

   b I'll turn the __*fan*__ on – it's hot in here. *S*

1 a Their faces light up with pleasure.

   b My e-book reader weighs just 170 grams – it's very _____ . ___

2 a They have been inseparable all their lives.

   b My grandmother _____ next door to us. ___

3 a Sydney would suffer anything to spare Charlie.

   b Come and stay with us – you can sleep in the _____ bedroom. ___

4 a One good turn deserves another.

   b Chaplin began performing at the _____ of the century. ___

5 a He negotiated his brother's first million-dollar contract in 1917.

   b Metal will expand if you heat it, and _____ when it cools down. ___

6 a My father was always on my back about working hard at school.

   b He was a _____ man to get along with. ___

7 a I'm sorry, but I don't really understand what you mean.

   b I don't think he's generous. On the contrary, he's very _____ . ___

8 a When I was a boy, I used to go fishing with my uncle.

   b I didn't have a pen, so I _____ a pencil instead. ___

9 a I've just read a fascinating book about identical twins.

   b The restaurant gets busy, so you'll need to _____ a table. ___

10 a The big wheel is the only ride I'll go on at the fair.

   b She's got lovely long _____ hair. ___

Vocabulary

Wordlist on page 207 of the Coursebook

A Adjectives of personality

1 Match the descriptions **1–8** to an adjective from the box.

| affectionate ambitious bossy clumsy dull fussy reserved stubborn |

1 She worries too much about detail. _____
2 He's always telling people what to do. _____
3 She keeps dropping things. _____
4 He won't change his mind. _____
5 She's a bit boring. _____
6 You never know what he's thinking or feeling. _____
7 She wants to get to the top of her profession. _____
8 He never stops kissing his girlfriend. _____

2 Complete the sentences with the correct form of the words in capitals at the end of each line. You may need to write a negative form.

1 Stop being so _____ and think about others for a change! **SELF**
2 You can't trust Paul to do a good job – he's very _____ . **RELY**
3 She's got long _____ hair which comes down to her waist. **FLOW**
4 Sally's so _____ – she gets upset at the slightest criticism. **SENSE**
5 Come on, hurry up and make a choice! Don't be so _____ . **DECIDE**
6 Such smooth skin – hard to believe my face used to be _____ . **SPOT**
7 Learn to be more _____ and accept that people are different. **TOLERATE**
8 Why is our meal taking so long? I'm getting _____ now. **PATIENCE**

Language focus

Grammar reference on page 214 of the Coursebook

A Causative passive

Write sentences using the prompts and the correct form of causative *have* or *get*. Add any other necessary words.

0 I / have / coat / dry-clean / week ago
   I had my coat dry-cleaned a week ago.

1 We / have / car / repair / yesterday
   _____

2 I want / get / my ears / pierce
   _____

3 She / never / have / teeth / whiten / before
   _____

4 I / get / hair / cut / 5 o'clock / tomorrow
   _____

5 They / probably / have / house / paint / next month
   _____

6 I / always / have / my suits / make / Milan / now
   _____

B Phrasal verbs

There are four types of phrasal verb.

1 Intransitive verbs – verbs not followed by a direct object	e.g. *to grow up* *Of course I know Portsmouth. That's where I grew up.*
2 Transitive separable verbs the direct object can go: – before the particle (i.e. it separates the verb from the particle) – or after the particle (the object pronoun can only go before the particle)	e.g. *to let someone down* *You have let the whole school down.* *You have let down the whole school.* *You have let us down.* *(NOT: You have let down us.)*
3 Transitive inseparable verbs – the direct object can only go after the particle (i.e. it cannot separate the verb from the particle) – the object pronoun can only go after the particle	e.g. *to fall for someone* *I fell for Gillian the moment I saw her.* *(NOT: I fell Gillian for.)* *I fell for her.* *(NOT: I fell her for.)*
4 Transitive inseparable verbs with two particles – the same rules apply as for transitive inseparable verbs with one particle	e.g. *to go out with someone* *She wants to go out with Ewan.* *She wants to go out with him.*

Deciding which type a verb is

In many dictionaries the position of someone (or something) in the infinitive will tell you if the verb is separable or inseparable.

Separable		Inseparable
to let someone down (type 2) (*someone* appears between the verb and the particle)	or	*to fall for someone* (type 3) (*someone* appears after the particle) *to go out with someone* (type 4)

The verbs in the following exercise all appear in the Phrasal verb list on pages 130–131. One sentence in each of the following pairs contains a mistake which is related to the use of the phrasal verb. Rewrite the incorrect sentence to make it correct.

1 a I'm very fond of my grandmother. I've always looked her up to.

　b My boyfriend was getting too serious so I decided to split up with him.

_____

2 a I think I take my father after rather than my mother.

　b We haven't taken to the new science teacher; he's much stricter than Mr Lee.

_____

3 a Liz and Sue have fallen out again; Liz borrowed Sue's watch without asking.

　b I don't earn a great deal but I get it by.

_____

4 a I blame the parents. They haven't brought up him very well.

　b The head teacher told me off for running in the corridor.

_____

5 a I still haven't got over the shock of my ex-girlfriend marrying my cousin.

　b It was a tough interview but I think I got it through OK.

_____

C Relative clauses

Complete the sentences with appropriate relative pronouns, giving alternatives where more than one answer is possible. Add commas if necessary.

1 Mr Jones _____ has taught here for 15 years will be leaving the school at the end of term. He has accepted the post of head teacher at St Mary's, the school in _____ he began his teaching career in 1990.

2 **A:** Yesterday I spoke to the boy _____ has just moved into the house on the corner.

   B: Do you mean the one _____ mum looks like Meryl Streep?

3 **A:** Do you know a good place _____ we could go for an Indian meal?

   B: Yes, we could go to that restaurant _____ has just opened in Farndale Street.

4 The reason _____ we're going skiing in March is because it's much cheaper then. Obviously we'd prefer to go in January _____ the snow's better, but we can't afford it.

5 The fox _____ is normally a very shy animal can often be seen in city centres. It tends to keep to residential areas _____ food is usually easy to find.

6 You're the only student _____ hasn't written the essay. What's more, it's the third piece of homework in a row _____ you haven't done.

7 I lost that necklace _____ I was wearing on Friday _____ made me very unpopular at home. It belonged to my eldest sister _____ boyfriend gave it to her for her birthday.

Reading and Use of English

Part 4

Transformations

For questions **1–6**, complete the second sentence so that it has a similar meaning to the first sentence, using the word given. **Do not change the word given.** You must use between **two** and **five** words, including the word given. Write your answers **IN CAPITAL LETTERS**.

1 Someone broke into our house last night.

   HAD

   We _____ last night.

2 I want them to dye my hair red at the hairdresser's.

   HAVE

   I want _____ red at the hairdresser's.

3 I have a great deal of respect for Susie, so I asked her.

   WHOM

   I asked Susie, _____ a great deal of respect.

4 Naomi is the girl who lent me a ruler during the exam.

   WHOSE

   Naomi is the girl _____ during the exam.

5 My grandfather is the person I most admire.

   LOOK

   The person I most _____ my grandfather.

6 His parents said he was a disappointment to them and they expected his behaviour to improve.

   DOWN

   His parents said he had _____ and they expected his behaviour to improve.

Multiple-choice cloze

For questions **1–8**, read the text below and decide which answer (**A**, **B**, **C** or **D**) best fits each gap. There is an example at the beginning (**0**).

Home-alone fathers

The number of (**0**) _____ fathers has increased considerably in recent years in Britain. We spoke to one such dad, Steve Baker, about how he (**1**) _____ it all. Steve, 43, has (**2**) _____ up his two teenage sons since he and his wife (**3**) _____ up two years ago.

'It's no (**4**) _____ difficult for a man than it is for a woman,' says Steve. 'It's a full-time job, whoever you are. Fortunately for me, my employers were very (**5**) _____ in the first few months and they let me take time off work to get myself organized. As (**6**) _____ as the housework is concerned, I don't mind cooking, as I've always been good at that; it's the ironing I can't (**7**) _____ ! Generally speaking, the boys and I get on very well together but, of course, sometimes we have rows. That's when I really (**8**) _____ having someone there with me to help me out.'

0	**A** alone	**B** only	**C** <u>single</u>	**D** unique
1	**A** gets by	**B** copes with	**C** looks after	**D** takes care
2	**A** taken	**B** made	**C** grown	**D** brought
3	**A** divorced	**B** separated	**C** parted	**D** split
4	**A** very	**B** more	**C** much	**D** at all
5	**A** comprehensive	**B** understandable	**C** sympathetic	**D** supported
6	**A** far	**B** well	**C** much	**D** soon
7	**A** support	**B** hate	**C** stand	**D** help
8	**A** miss	**B** regret	**C** want	**D** need

Open cloze

For questions **1–8**, read the text below and think of the word which best fits each gap. Use only **one** word in each gap. There is an example at the beginning (**0**). Write your answers **IN CAPITAL LETTERS**.

Sleepovers

The sleepover has worked (**0**) _ITS_ way into our culture from the United States. It is particularly popular among pre-adolescent and adolescent girls, (**1**) _____ parents are persuaded to open their house up, often to whole groups of youngsters intent on (**2**) _____ fun. It consists of children inviting their friends round to stay for the night, and doing the kinds of things that children like to do together. Precisely (**3**) _____ that involves depends, to a large extent, (**4**) _____ the age of the children, but it generally means tired parents having to put (**5**) _____ with noise and unruly behaviour until the early hours of the morning.

Some schools are opposed to sleepovers and many send out letters asking parents (**6**) _____ to organize them during term time. Even though sleepover parties normally (**7**) _____ place at weekends, they can still affect pupils' ability to concentrate at school during the week. It is not unusual (**8**) _____ children to sleep for just an hour or two at a sleepover and it can take them several days to recover.

Writing
Part 1

Essay

1 Read the following Part 1 instructions and the model answer below, then answer these questions.

1 Does the writer agree or disagree with the statement?

2 Does the writer

a offer arguments both for and against the statement or

b offer only arguments which support his or her general opinion?

In your English class you have been talking about the generation gap. Now, your English teacher has asked you to write an essay.

You will see the essay title and some notes you have written on the right. Write an essay using **all** the notes and give reasons for your point of view.

Essay question

Parents can never fully understand their teenage children's problems. Do you agree?

Notes

Write about:

1 difference in age between parents and children

2 problems faced by teenagers now and in the past

3 .... (your own idea

Write your **essay** in **140–190** words.

Children often go through difficult times during their teenage years. Although some parents fail to provide support, many others are able to understand their child's problems and give them the help they need.

Firstly, parents' age is an advantage. Because they are much older than their children, they are usually also wiser and able to give an objective opinion on the problems they face. They can see the issue from the outside and offer advice which is not affected by emotions.

Moreover, most teenage problems nowadays are related to relationships, something which was also true in the past. Consequently, many parents know exactly what their children are feeling as they have had similar experiences themselves.

Finally, the Internet means that parents are more able than ever to understand the problems of young people. They can discuss issues with and get help from other parents in online forums and chats, tools which did not exist when they were teenagers.

To sum up, it is not true that parents are incapable of understanding their teenage children's problems. If they have not been in similar situations themselves, they can always look online for help.

2 What point does the writer make for 'your own idea', number 3 in the Notes section in exercise **1**?

3 The writer of the answer in exercise **1** makes good use of a range of linking words and expressions. Underline the linking devices.

<u>Although</u> some parents fail ...

4 Do one of the following tasks, **a** or **b**. Write your answer in **140–190** words.

 a Write your own answer to the question in exercise **1** on page 50, agreeing with the statement.

 b Write an answer to the following question. If you choose this option, do exercises **5** and **6** in the **Before you write** box before you plan and write your answer.

In your English class you have been talking about marriage. Now, your English teacher has asked you to write an essay.

You will see the essay title and some notes you have written on the right. Write your essay using **all** the notes and give reasons for your point of view.

Essay question

It is better to wait until you are at least 30 before you get married. Do you agree?

Notes

Write about:

1 life as a single person

2 economic factors

3 .... (your own idea)

Before you write

The following tasks are designed to give you ideas when planning your answer to the question in **4b** above.

5 Match **a–f** to points **1** and **2**.

 1 life as a single person _____

 2 economic factors _a,_____

 a I can't afford to get married yet – the cost of a wedding is far too high.

 b I want to be single for as long as possible – you have much more freedom to do what you want.

 c Living with someone else is cheaper than living on your own, so we're getting married sooner rather than later.

 d I want to get married as soon as possible – I don't want to be on my own and lonely.

 e If I leave it too late, I'll have trouble finding a partner and I'll be single for the rest of my life.

 f I'm not earning enough to buy a house and bring up children. I can save money by living with my parents.

6 Point 3 in the Notes section asks you to give your own idea. Match the statements **a–f** to the appropriate couple, **A** or **B**.

Couple A: We got married in our early twenties. _____

Couple B: We got married in our mid-thirties. _a,_____

 a By that time, we'd each been in enough relationships – both short-term and long-term – to know for certain that we were made for each other.

 b We wanted to have children while we were still young enough to enjoy them. We didn't want to be 'old parents'.

 c We were wiser, more mature and felt able to make the marriage last.

 d We loved each other and even though we were still at university, we knew we wanted to spend the rest of our lives together.

 e For the previous ten years, we'd each worked in a number of different places. We were both settled in our jobs and happy in the town where we lived.

 f In our country it's normal for people to marry young. We just did what everyone else does.

Multiple matching

1 You are going to read a magazine article in which four people are interviewed. For questions **1–10**, choose from the people **(A–D)**. The people may be chosen more than once.

Which of the people says the following?

I have made unsuccessful complaints.	**1**
I get on very well with the people below.	**2**
I lived in the flat before I decided to buy it.	**3**
I do not often have problems because of noisy customers.	**4**
The character of the area has changed for the worse.	**5**
My sleep was often interrupted.	**6**
I used to have perfect working conditions.	**7**
I intend to go and live somewhere else.	**8**
A lot of people I know make the wrong assumptions.	**9**
I am a regular customer down below.	**10**

Living above a shop

Living above a shop may be handy if you need something in a hurry, but it also has its disadvantages.
Lynn Haywood *spoke to four people with a story to tell.*

A Gwen Crowley I bought my flat in Chelsea with some money I inherited. I've been here since the 1970s when I rented it from a friend of a friend. By the 80s I'd fallen in love with it and just had to have it for myself. It's on the King's Road, a bustling shopping street with fantastic amenities, all of which are right on my doorstep. I live above a supermarket, which was a nuisance at first; I was regularly woken up by people stacking shelves at night, and then, of course, there were the early morning deliveries. I always refused to set foot in the place and would buy all my food further down the road. However, the owners were very reasonable when I complained and they sound-proofed the ceiling, which really cut down the noise. Now I shop there almost every day.

B Paul Burton When I first moved here I had the peace and quiet I needed to write the novel I was working on. The shop below sold wool and knitting accessories and there was a butcher's, a baker's and one or two other specialist shops in the street. They've all gone now, unfortunately; they couldn't compete with the out-of-town shopping malls and supermarkets which were springing up everywhere. The wool shop turned into a hairdresser's and now, you wouldn't believe what I have to put up with. If it isn't loud music, it's the television at full volume, and then there's everyone shouting above the noise of the hairdryers. I've had a moan at them about it on more than one occasion, but they just ignore me.

C Judie Marland Everyone thinks that living above a pub must be a nightmare. I've been lucky, though; the landlord of the pub is very considerate and, apart from the occasional drunk singing outside at midnight, so are the people who drink there. A few years ago the landlord and I came to an agreement that he wouldn't play music above a certain volume after 10 o'clock. After a while he decided to cut out music altogether, and all I hear now is a gentle hum of conversation coming up through the floor. Many of my friends take it for granted that I must spend a lot of time in there, but I won't go into pubs on my own and my boyfriend always wants to go to his favourite place in the town centre.

D Arthur Short It's the smell which has forced me to put my flat up for sale. Fish and chip shops are, by their nature, very smelly and there is no way I or the owner can do anything about it, so there's no point complaining. In fact, I'm on first-name terms with everyone down there and I often pop in to say hello, though never to buy anything – I don't think I'll ever eat fish and chips again as long as I live! It's noisy, but that isn't a problem; this is a lively part of town and I've always preferred places where I can hear people coming and going. I'll be sad to move out, but I'm tired of friends screwing their faces up and holding their noses every time they come and visit me. I've got my eye on a flat down in the port area – it's busy and there are some great views out to sea.

2 Find the phrasal verbs **1–6** in the text. The letters in brackets refer to the relevant paragraphs. Match the phrasal verbs to the meanings **a–f**.

1 cut down (A)	**a** stop (playing/doing/eating, etc.)
2 spring up (B)	**b** tolerate
3 turn into (B)	**c** stop living in a house/flat
4 put up with (B)	**d** reduce
5 cut out (C)	**e** become (something different)
6 move out (D)	**f** appear suddenly

3 Complete the sentences with the correct form of an appropriate phrasal verb from exercise **2**.
1 There were clear blue skies at first, but then it _____ a really horrible day.
2 It's so noisy here; I don't know how you _____ it.
3 They had a big row, after which Jim _____ and went to live with his mother.
4 Not so long ago there were no children's clothes shops in the town; now they're _____ all over the place.
5 The doctor says he should _____ on the amount of coffee he drinks, but he doesn't have to _____ caffeine altogether.

4 Find expressions in the text which have the following meanings. The letters in brackets refer to the relevant paragraphs.
1 I would never go in (A) _____
2 I've complained to them (B) _____
3 made a decision together (C) _____
4 advertise that we want to sell (D) _____
5 I'm friendly with (D) _____
6 I'm interested in buying (D) _____

Vocabulary

Wordlist on page 207 of the Coursebook

A Shopping

1 Find 14 words related to shopping in the wordsearch and write them in the spaces given below. There are seven shopkeepers and seven things you find in a shop or a supermarket. The words go forwards or backwards, up or down, or diagonally.

T	T	T	S	I	R	O	L	F	G
F	R	T	I	I	E	A	E	R	C
R	O	N	G	L	L	A	O	G	H
E	L	E	O	F	L	C	E	R	E
T	L	G	O	I	E	H	L	E	C
N	E	A	D	R	W	E	S	H	K
U	Y	S	S	S	E	C	I	C	O
O	H	W	A	H	J	K	A	T	U
C	H	E	M	I	S	T	A	U	T
C	N	N	I	A	G	R	A	B	T

1 _____   8 _____
2 _____   9 _____
3 _____   10 _____
4 _____   11 _____
5 _____   12 _____
6 _____   13 _____
7 _____   14 _____

2 In sentences **1–10**, decide which answer (**A**, **B**, **C** or **D**) best fits each gap.

1 If you decide you don't like it, bring it back and we'll give you a _____ .

   A receipt   **B** refund   **C** guarantee   **D** reward

2 I'm sorry, we don't have any in stock at the moment, but they are on _____ .

   A request   **B** demand   **C** order   **D** ask

3 You get good _____ for money in this store – quality products at competitive prices.

   A worth   **B** price   **C** value   **D** cost

4 They didn't have any _____ peas; only tinned or frozen.

   A fresh   **B** convenient   **C** new   **D** recent

5 If it's not working, take it back to the shop. They have to replace _____ goods by law.

   A mistaken   **B** faulty   **C** lazy   **D** incorrect

6 Do you like my new dress? I bought it in the January _____ .

   A cuts   **B** discounts   **C** bargains   **D** sales

7 I only got the cheese because it was on _____ ; it was £5 a kilo instead of £7.

   A offer   **B** reduction   **C** counter   **D** impulse

8 It says £5.60 on the label. You've _____ me £6.50.

   A taken   **B** deducted   **C** reduced   **D** charged

9 I have to buy Doggy Chunks for Fifi; she won't eat any other _____ of dog food.

   A selection   **B** brand   **C** mark   **D** variation

10 This car was the most expensive purchase I've ever _____ .

   A made   **B** taken   **C** put   **D** done

B Towns and villages

1 Choose an adjective from the box to describe each of the places in **1–5**.

bustling	depressing	prosperous	quaint	run-down

1 This is a wealthy town, with many successful businesses and high-quality housing.
_____

2 We loved the market, a lively place full of people, noise and activity.
_____

3 This inner-city area has been neglected, and the buildings are in very poor condition. _____

4 It's an attractive village, unusual and rather old-fashioned. _____

5 The grey Victorian buildings have the same effect on me as the miserable weather.
_____

2 Write the word from the box that can be used with each set of three words to form common collocations.

area	block	~~centre~~	estate	site	street

0	town	shopping	leisure	_centre_
1	office	apartment	tower	_____
2	pedestrian	shopping	one-way	_____
3	building	caravan	historic	_____
4	residential	conservation	rural	_____
5	industrial	housing	real	_____

C Paraphrasing

Complete the pairs of sentences with prepositions. The sentence pairs have the same meaning.

0 He's staring _into_ space. He's looking straight ahead _at_ nothing.

1 She's gone ____ search of food. She's gone to look ____ food.

2 We don't know that ____ certain. We can't be sure ____ that.

3 The conversation turned ____ sport. People started talking ____ sport.

4 Get rid ____ those children! Make those children go away ____ here!

5 The banks are to blame ____ this crisis. The banks are the cause ____ this crisis.

Language focus

 Grammar reference on page 215 of the Coursebook

A Present perfect simple, present perfect continuous and past simple

Complete the sentences with the present perfect simple, present perfect continuous or past simple form of the verbs in brackets.

1 Over the last century, life expectancy in Britain _____ (increase) dramatically. At the beginning of the 1900s men generally _____ (expect) to live to 45, while women _____ (live) four years longer. Since then the figure _____ (rise) to 78 and 82 respectively.

2 In the last ten years we _____ (move) house no fewer than six times, and so far during this period we _____ (never/stay) in the same place for more than two years. The first time we _____ (sell) our house, we'd only been living there for nine months; then my dad _____ (change) his job and we _____ (move) around the country ever since.

3 My friend Alice is 84 years old and I _____ (know) her since we were at school together. I _____ (try) to get in touch with her all afternoon. I _____ (phone) her four times but there's no answer. It's half past four now and she said she'd be at home at this time, so I'm beginning to worry something _____ (happen) to her. It's all a bit strange, because I _____ (go) to see her this morning and she _____ (seem) fine.

4 Sorry, Jean, I'll have to go now. My son _____ (just/walk) in through the door. He _____ (play) football all morning and he's absolutely filthy. He _____ (make) friends with a group of older boys last week and he _____ (go) to the park with them every day.

5 Ever since I _____ (retire), I _____ (be) so busy! For one thing, I _____ (take) up gardening again. I _____ (lay) a new lawn last week and I _____ (put) up a new fence this morning – I hope to finish it this afternoon.

B Correcting mistakes

Find the mistakes in the following sentences and correct them.

1 My father's been worked as a shop assistant for over 15 years.

2 I've been breaking my leg three times in the last few years.

3 Charlie Chaplin has been one of the greatest comic actors of the silent movies.

4 Do you realize how long time I've been waiting here for you?

5 This is the first time I see this film.

6 James and I have known each other since many years.

7 It's over two years since I play football.

8 I cleaned three rooms of the house so far today; I'll do the other two this afternoon.

C Expressing preferences

Complete the sentences with words from the box. There are three extra words you do not need to use.

| had | much | not | prefer | rather | than | to | very | would |

1 Carmen prefers reading books _____ watching films.
2 What would you _____ do tonight – eat at home or go out to a restaurant?
3 I'd prefer to look for a job rather _____ go to university.
4 I'd rather _____ go for a walk today, if you don't mind.
5 Paul says he _____ rather watch paint dry than go to see a ballet.
6 Laura doesn't want to go out today. She'd _____ rather stay at home.

Reading and Use of English
Part 1

Multiple-choice cloze

For questions **1–8**, read the text below and decide which answer (**A**, **B**, **C** or **D**) best fits each gap. There is an example at the beginning (**0**).

Money-making houses

If times are hard and you are **(0)** ___ of cash, your house might **(1)** ___ you with the solution to your problem.

Renting out a **(2)** ___ room in your house can be a good way of making extra money. What's more, a government scheme **(3)** ___ you to receive up to £4,250 each year from lodgers without paying tax. You could also install solar panels on your roof and become self-sufficient in electricity. If you produce enough, you can **(4)** ___ sell some back to the National Grid. You won't make a huge **(5)** ___ of money, but it is satisfying to know that the electricity in your house is green.

Offering your house as a film location is another possibility, as **(6)** ___ as you don't mind having 30 to 40 people in your living room for a week, changing the furniture round, painting your walls a different colour and **(7)** ___ the neighbours by parking enormous lorries in the street outside. It's certainly a **(8)** ___ option, giving you the chance to earn hundreds of pounds each day.

0	**A** lacking	**B** broke	**C** short	**D** poor
1	**A** offer	**B** provide	**C** give	**D** propose
2	**A** further	**B** bonus	**C** second	**D** spare
3	**A** accepts	**B** agrees	**C** allows	**D** lets
4	**A** even	**B** still	**C** yet	**D** until
5	**A** number	**B** amount	**C** range	**D** total
6	**A** far	**B** much	**C** soon	**D** long
7	**A** animating	**B** arguing	**C** upsetting	**D** working up
8	**A** disposable	**B** rentable	**C** profitable	**D** considerable

Open cloze

For questions **1–8**, read the text below and think of the word which best fits each gap. Use only **one** word in each gap. There is an example at the beginning **(0)**. Write your answers **IN CAPITAL LETTERS**.

My favourite shop

Many people have a shop they love to go back to again and again, **(0)** _WHERE_ the pleasure comes as much from browsing **(1)** _____ from buying.

My own favourite is Hamleys, 'the finest toy shop **(2)** _____ the world', situated in Regent Street, **(3)** _____ walking distance of the hotel where I usually stay during my regular visits to London. For me, and I'm sure for many others, **(4)** _____ trip to the capital would be complete without spending time in this seven-storey toy paradise.

Hamleys has **(5)** _____ in business for over 250 years, and I have been a customer **(6)** _____ my oldest daughter was a baby. My two children are grown **(7)** _____ now and have both left home, but I still go there to look around and take in the atmosphere. I could spend hours **(8)** _____ end just strolling round the store, watching the assistants demonstrate the latest toys. I still make the occasional purchase, perhaps for my young nephew, or even for myself. I am just a child at heart.

Word formation

For questions **1–8**, read the text below. Use the word given in capitals at the end of some of the lines to form a word that fits in the gap in the same line. There is an example at the beginning **(0)**. Write your answers **IN CAPITAL LETTERS**.

Village life

In 2004, tired of the noise and **(0)** _POLLUTION_ of the city,	**POLLUTE**
best-selling author Will Smith and his family moved out to Chersey, a	
(1) _____ village set in magnificent countryside, with 53	**PICTURE**
(2) _____ and one shop. Three years later they sold their	**INHABIT**
(3) _____ 16th-century cottage and moved back to London,	**BEAUTY**
where they now live in a smart new neighbourhood on the outskirts	
of the city. So what happened? 'Chersey seemed an idyllic place	
to live,' explains Will, 'a quiet, peaceful old village in extremely	
(4) _____ surroundings. However, we soon became aware	**PLEASE**
of a number of **(5)** _____ of village life. With so little to	**ADVANTAGE**
do in Chersey, and because the buses were so **(6)** _____ ,	**FREQUENT**
our teenage children became **(7)** _____ on us to take them	**DEPEND**
everywhere in the car. As for our own social life, the neighbours were	
rather cold and **(8)** _____ , so we felt rather isolated and	**FRIEND**
lonely. It was not the rural idyll we had expected.'	

Transformations

For questions **1–6**, complete the second sentence so that it has a similar meaning to the first sentence, using the word given. **Do not change the word given**. You must use between **two** and **five** words, including the word given. Write only the missing words **IN CAPITAL LETTERS**.

1 I had my hair cut a month ago.
   SINCE
   It _____ I had my hair cut.

2 We haven't seen each other for ten years.
   LAST
   The _____ each other was ten years ago.

3 I'd prefer to leave later if you don't mind.
   YET
   I'd rather _____ if you don't mind.

4 I'd rather walk than catch a bus.
   RATHER
   I'd prefer _____ a bus.

5 It is not the government's fault that there is an economic crisis.
   BLAME
   The government is _____ the economic crisis.

6 Lucy only started sweating when the race had finished.
   INTO
   Lucy _____ sweat until after the race had finished.

Review

1 Read the following Part 2 instructions.
   You have seen this notice in an English-language magazine.

Reviews needed!

Is there a website you particularly like using? If so, could you write a review of it? Tell us what you use it for and why you like it, and mention anything you don't find quite so useful. We'd also like to know who you'd recommend the site to.

The best reviews will be published next month.

Write your **review** for the magazine in **140–190** words.

A Structure

Read the model answer and match the summaries **a–d** to one of the paragraphs.

a Useful features
b Recommendation
c Features the writer does not find useful
d The website and reasons for using it

> **Amazon**
>
> 1 I love reading and listening to music and I normally buy my books and CDs from Amazon. The prices are always extremely competitive and the service is fast and efficient: sometimes an order can arrive the next day.
>
> 2 What I find particularly useful about the website are the customer reviews, which are usually very informative. There are often several of these for one book or CD, so you get a fairly good idea of what something is like. I also like the fact that Amazon gives you recommendations of what to buy next, based on the books or music you have already ordered.
>
> 3 It sells a range of other items, too, including cameras, domestic appliances and sports equipment, but personally, I prefer going to shops for those kinds of things. You can also download books and music from the site, but as I don't have an e-book reader or an MP3 player, it's not a service I use.
>
> 4 I'd recommend the site to anyone who shares my interests. It's especially handy if, like me, you prefer print versions to e-books but don't live near a decent bookshop.

B Language analysis

1 Read the model answer again and answer the following questions.
   1 Which adjectives are used to describe the positive features?
      competitive, …
   2 Which words are used to modify adjectives?
      extremely (competitive), …
   3 Which adverbs of frequency are used?
      normally, …

2 Complete the sentences from the model answer.
   1 What I find particularly useful _____ the website are the customer reviews.
   2 I also like the _____ that Amazon gives you recommendations.
   3 _____ , I prefer going to shops for those kinds of things.
   4 I'd recommend the site to _____ who shares my interests.

C Planning your review

Now plan your own review, following these steps.

1 Decide which website you are going to write about.
   Choose one you know reasonably well and make notes under the following headings:
   • What I use it for
   • Why I like it
   • Features I don't find useful
   • Who I would recommend it to

2 Decide on a few adjectives you could use to describe the positive features.

3 Write your **review** in **140–190** words. Follow the paragraph plan in **A** and include relevant language from **B**.

⑧ Up and away

Multiple choice

1 You are going to read an article about a cruise to Australia. For questions **1–6**, choose the answer (**A**, **B**, **C** or **D**) which you think fits best according to the text.

Destination Australia

*Forget long-distance flights and take the boat if you want to arrive in Australia full of energy. You might even enjoy the holiday of a lifetime on the way, says **Jan Etherington**.*

My son, Tom, made the announcement on New Year's Eve. 'Fran and I are getting married … ' Hurrah! ' … in Australia.' Now, I've always wanted to go to Australia but like most people, I'm **put off** by the flight and the thought of arriving pale, exhausted and needing a week to recover. Even with a stopover, you face two long-distance flights. But it doesn't have to be like that. I found a way to arrive suntanned, refreshed, and ready for action. I went by boat, on the *Saga Rose* world cruise.

If I'd had the time and money, I could have gone all the way round the world, but the great thing about this cruise is that you can embark and disembark wherever you wish. If you want to get to Australia or New Zealand, take a shorter flight somewhere, join the world cruise and arrive in civilized style. I **picked** it **up** in Valparaiso (the port for Santiago, Chile) and sailed on from there to Sydney.

The *Saga Rose* is a good-looking ship. Launched in 1965, she is highly regarded by maritime experts for her elegant lines. Passenger capacity is 587, but we were fewer than 400, with 350, largely Filipino, crew who were smart, efficient and full of good humour. It was the cleanest ship I'd ever seen and the variety and freshness of the meals was impressive, with a welcome freedom to dine in the evening at any time between 7.15 and 9pm.

I met lots of accomplished, funny, clever, attractive people on the ship. Good company and a well-run ship are important, because, on this stretch of the journey, we were together for a month – long enough to learn a skill. I **took up** salsa, inspired by dance teacher, Thabo, who made us believe we were good enough to perform in front of passengers and crew.

Julia's jewellery-making classes were surprisingly popular. Even cynics (like me) were impressed as, using seeds and beads from local sources, students produced desirable costume jewellery. And the watercolour classes gave amateurs the tools to capture the passing scenes more imaginatively than with a digital camera.

Each day brought a once-in-a-lifetime experience. From Santiago, we sailed west, across the South Pacific. As we neared each island, usually at dawn, peering sleepily through binoculars, the dot on the horizon would slowly form a personality. There were no two alike. Easter Island was soft, undulating, like a huge, warm, green pillow. But the knowledge that the islanders had **used up** their resources and destroyed their environment, by their obsessive building of the giant Moai statues, lent it a terrible sadness and mystery. Tahiti looks as if it needs ironing. The volcanic hills are jagged and sharp. Lush and green, it is full of waterfalls and wild forests. A dramatic place, it seems conscious of its role as the most important island in French Polynesia.

Each Pacific island is a long way from its neighbour, which meant many 'sea days'. These proved a lovely way to **catch up on** reading and while away hours scanning the horizon, where every wave appeared to be a whale or a dolphin. I kept fit by walking the promenade deck every morning (seven circuits is a mile), swimming in the seawater pool and forgoing puddings and cakes (I had a wedding outfit to get into).

As we cruised into Sydney at sunrise, it was like sailing into a familiar postcard. We passed the Opera House, slid under the Harbour Bridge and, on the quayside, Tom and Fran waved banners of welcome. I leapt off, relaxed, fit and full of energy. 'Let's go shopping for a hat!'

1 In the first paragraph we learn that the writer
   A does not like travel.
   B was not in very good health.
   C had not been to Australia before.
   D had not seen her son for a long time.
2 What, according to the writer, is the main advantage of the *Saga Rose* cruise?
   A It offers the traveller flexibility.
   B It is more affordable than flying.
   C It takes the traveller right round the world.
   D It is more comfortable than other cruises.
3 The writer says she was pleased that
   A the ship was not completely full.
   B the crew was mainly Filipino.
   C she could choose her evening meal time.
   D she had decided to travel alone.
4 The writer says she had not expected
   A to have to spend so long on board the ship.
   B to get on so well with her fellow travellers.
   C to enjoy the organized activities so much.
   D to see such good results from one of the classes.
5 What does the writer say about the islands in the South Pacific?
   A She only ever saw them from a distance.
   B They were all very different from each other.
   C There were two that she did not particularly like.
   D She would not choose to return to any of them.
6 Whilst sailing through the South Pacific, the writer says
   A she spent a long time on board ship.
   B she saw a wide variety of marine life.
   C she was able to go swimming in the sea.
   D she ate a large amount of sweet food.

2 Match the phrasal verbs in **bold** in the text with the meanings **a–e**. Use the context to help you. The meanings are in the infinitive form.

   a start doing a new activity _____
   b spend time doing an activity you have not had time to do recently _____
   c make you decide not to do something _____
   d finish a supply of something _____
   e join and follow a journey or route _____

3 Complete the extracts from the text **1–5** with a preposition. Then check your answers in the text.
   1 I found a way to arrive suntanned, refreshed, and ready _____ action. I went _____ boat, _____ the *Saga Rose* world cruise.
   2 ... the variety and freshness _____ the meals was impressive, _____ a welcome freedom to dine _____ the evening _____ any time _____ 7.15 and 9pm.
   3 ... _____ this stretch of the journey, we were together _____ a month ...
   4 From Santiago, we sailed west, _____ the South Pacific. As we neared each island, usually _____ dawn, peering sleepily _____ binoculars, the dot _____ the horizon would slowly form a personality.
   5 Lush and green, it is full _____ waterfalls and wild forests. A dramatic place, it seems conscious _____ its role as the most important island _____ French Polynesia.

Vocabulary

Wordlist on pages 207–208 of the Coursebook

A Travel

Underline the correct alternative.

1 Everyone thought the holiday was great *fun/funny* but I didn't have such a good time.
2 The area near the palace gates was *full/crowded* with tourists.
3 The facilities on this *camping/campsite* are excellent.
4 Have you decided where you're going on *holiday/holidays* yet?
5 We always *stay/live* in the same hotel when we go to London.
6 All the hotels at the ski *station/resort* are fully booked, unfortunately.
7 We didn't bring back any *souvenirs/memories* from our holiday. We didn't see anything worth buying.
8 From the top of the cathedral tower there are some spectacular *sights/sites/views* of the surrounding countryside.
9 The cost of the *trip/journey/travel* includes two nights in a four-star hotel with half board.
10 She didn't enjoy the Mediterranean *voyage/cruise/tour* at all; she was seasick most of the time.

B Phrasal verbs

Complete the sentences with phrasal verbs from the box.

catch on	come across	get about	head for	turn out

1 I've never _____ such a horrible person in all my life!
2 A huge crowd is expected to _____ to see the president give his speech.
3 The island is very small and the best way to _____ is by bicycle.
4 It's very hot here in July, so we usually get out of the city and _____ the beach or the mountains.
5 When he commented on the level of noise at the party, I didn't _____ to what he meant at first. Then I realized it was his way of saying he wanted to leave.

C Sleep

Complete the sentences with either the infinitive with *to* or the gerund form of words from the box.

fall	~~get~~	nod	sleep	stay	take

0 It took me ages __*to get*__ to sleep last night.
1 Are you planning on _____ a nap after lunch?
2 The speech was so boring I found it hard _____ awake.
3 It's not like Mike _____ asleep in front of the telly. He must have been exhausted.
4 I was so tired I kept _____ off during the film.
5 Don't phone me before 11 o'clock tomorrow morning – I'm going to try _____ in if I can.

Language focus

 Grammar reference on pages 215–216 of the Coursebook

The future

1 Each of the underlined future forms is inappropriate. Rewrite each sentence with a more suitable future form.

1 Have you cut your finger? Come into the bathroom and I <u>put</u> a plaster on it.

_____

2 Congratulations! I hear you <u>will have</u> a baby.

_____

3 I've arranged to play tennis with Miguel tomorrow morning. We'<u>re about to meet</u> at the sports centre at 10 am.

_____

4 Can you wake me up before you <u>will leave</u> for work tomorrow morning?

_____

5 I don't think I'<u>m getting</u> more than 50 per cent in tomorrow's exam; I never do well at Physics.

_____

6 This time tomorrow we'<u>re going to sit</u> on the plane, probably somewhere over France.

_____

7 What <u>do you do</u> next weekend? Have you made any plans?

_____

8 Phone me on Friday. I'<u>m speaking</u> to Greg by then, so I'll have more information.

_____

2 Complete the sentences with an appropriate future form of the verb in brackets.

1 That bag looks very heavy. I _____ (carry) it for you, if you want.

2 I _____ (have) my eyes tested on Saturday. My appointment's at 10.30.

3 The autumn term _____ (end) on December 23rd, the same day as my birthday. I _____ (be) 15 then.

4 No, don't phone me at 8 o'clock. I _____ (watch) the match at that time. Phone me at 9 instead; it _____ (finish) by then.

5 I _____ (get) some new clothes tomorrow; I want to change my look.

6 I think we should wait until Kevin _____ (get) back.

7 Don't forget that when they get here this evening, they _____ (travel) for over 12 hours, so I expect they _____ (want) to go straight to bed.

8 'Liz? Hi, it's Graham. Listen, I'm on the train at Croydon, so I _____ (be) at Brighton station at five past nine. Can you pick me up?'

3 In **1–5**, complete the first gap with a word from box **A** and the second gap with the correct form of a verb from box **B**.

A	B
after as by until when	finish get say set stop

1 'When can I watch TV?' 'Not _____ you _____ your homework.'

2 'When will the bats come out?' 'Not long _____ the sun _____ .'

3 'When shall we leave?' 'As soon _____ it _____ raining.'

4 'When can I eat my sweets?' 'Only _____ I _____ you can.'

5 'When will dinner be ready?' '_____ the time you _____ home, hopefully.'

Multiple-choice cloze

For questions **1–8**, read the text below and decide which answer (**A**, **B**, **C** or **D**) best fits each gap. There is an example at the beginning **(0)**.

Neil Armstrong

Astronaut Neil Armstrong's love of air **(0)** ___ began at a very early age. He was five years old when, in 1936, his father took him for his first flight in an aeroplane, a Ford Trimotor, also **(1)** ___ as the 'Tin Goose'. He had flying lessons whilst still at school and **(2)** ___ his pilot's licence aged just 15. After a period spent as a pilot in the navy, Armstrong finished his **(3)** ___ in aeronautical engineering at Purdue University and **(4)** ___ on to become an experimental research test pilot at Edwards Air Force Base. He flew rocket planes such as the X-15, in which he **(5)** ___ speeds of nearly 6,500 kilometres per hour.

In 1962 he became a NASA astronaut. He made just two trips into space, entering the history books on both **(6)** ___ . In 1966, as the command pilot for the Gemini 8 mission, he carried **(7)** ___ the first manned docking of two spacecraft. Then, on 20 July 1969, he stepped off the ladder of the lunar landing module *Eagle* and became the first man to **(8)** ___ foot on the surface of the Moon.

0	**A** journey	**B** trip	**C** <u>travel</u>	**D** voyage
1	**A** called	**B** titled	**C** known	**D** identified
2	**A** gained	**B** accomplished	**C** succeeded	**D** managed
3	**A** career	**B** study	**C** title	**D** degree
4	**A** applied	**B** changed	**C** went	**D** took
5	**A** arrived	**B** reached	**C** won	**D** earned
6	**A** times	**B** events	**C** occasions	**D** circumstances
7	**A** out	**B** up	**C** on	**D** away
8	**A** set	**B** put	**C** touch	**D** place

Open cloze

For questions **1–8**, read the text below and think of the word which best fits each gap. Use only **one** word in each gap. There is an example at the beginning **(0)**. Write your answers **IN CAPITAL LETTERS**.

A place in the sun

Southern Spain's Costa del Sol, which stretches from Nerja in the east to Manilva in the west, is one of the most famous tourist areas **(0)** _IN_ the world. Blessed with an average of 320 days of sunshine **(1)** _____ year, the coastline offers the perfect holiday destination for anyone wanting to switch off and unwind. As **(2)** _____ as its beautiful sun-soaked beaches and excellent gastronomy, the region boasts no fewer **(3)** _____ 30 golf courses, providing amateurs and professionals alike **(4)** _____ year-round golfing opportunities.

If you are looking for a more cultural experience, the city of Málaga **(5)** _____ well worth a visit. With its Roman theatre, Renaissance-style cathedral and Arab castle, Málaga is a historical centre on **(6)** _____ different peoples and cultures have left their mark over the centuries. It is also the birthplace of Picasso, **(7)** _____ house still stands today just a short distance from the Museo Picasso, **(8)** _____ of over 20 museums in the city.

Word formation

For questions **1–8**, read the text below. Use the word given in capitals at the end of some of the lines to form a word that fits in the gap in the same line. There is an example at the beginning **(0)**. Write your answers **IN CAPITAL LETTERS**.

Ageing adventurers

It was the end of an epic journey. In a **(0)** _PICTURESQUE_   **PICTURE**
harbour on the Caribbean island of St Maarten, Anthony Smith stood
on his raft, graciously accepting **(1)** _____ from a crowd   **CONGRATULATE**
of well-wishers on the quayside. The crowd seemed **(2)** _____   **FASCINATE**
by two things in particular: firstly, Mr Smith and his three-man British
crew had sailed the raft Antiki 2,600 miles across the Atlantic from
the Canary Islands, with a single sail and no engine. Secondly, Mr
Smith was 85 and the rest of the crew in their fifties and sixties. The
men, all with beards and many pounds **(3)** _____ than when   **LIGHT**
they set out 66 days before, looked tired but **(4)** _____ well   **SURPRISE**
after their **(5)** _____ journey. 'People said I was mad to do   **ORDINARY**
it at my age,' commented Mr Smith. 'But age is **(6)** _____ .'   **RELEVANT**
The four men knew that spending nearly ten weeks on a small craft
with few comforts could have been claustrophobic. But they insist
they had no serious **(7)** _____ . Their age helped, they   **AGREE**
believe, making them more **(8)** _____ of their differences   **TOLERATE**
and faults.

Transformations

For questions **1–6**, complete the second sentence so that it has a similar meaning to the first sentence, using the word given. **Do not change the word given.** You must use between **two** and **five** words, including the word given. There is an example at the beginning (**0**). Write your answers **IN CAPITAL LETTERS**.

> **Note!** Each of these transformations requires you to use a phrasal verb from Units **1–8**.

0 I've had enough of your rudeness.

PUT

I am not going _____ *TO PUT UP WITH* _____ your rudeness anymore.

1 I just can't wait to go on holiday!

LOOKING

I _____ on holiday!

2 They'll probably employ him for two months in the summer.

LIKELY

They _____ on for two months in the summer.

3 I think he's on the point of starting his own company.

SET

I think he's about _____ his own company.

4 Their relationship seems very good.

GET

It looks as _____ very well with each other.

5 Have you thought of a name for your dog yet?

COME

Have you _____ a name for your dog yet?

6 Sue and Alan ended their relationship a long time ago.

SPLIT

Sue and Alan _____ each other a long time ago.

Report

1 Read the following Part 2 instructions. You do not need to write an answer.

The school where you learn English has decided to organize a weekend trip to celebrate the end of the school year. You have been asked to write a report for the principal suggesting at least two places where you could spend the weekend. In your report you should explain why these places would be suitable for the trip.

Write your **report** in 140–190 words.

2 Read the answer on page 67 to the task in exercise **1**. Why are the underlined sentence beginnings **1–8** inappropriate for this report?

Introduction

(1) <u>What I'm going to do is</u> offer two suggestions for the end-of-year school trip.

Wickwood's Activity Centre

(2) <u>It'd be really cheap and fun if we went to</u> Wickwood's, the residential outdoor activity centre situated just 40 kilometres from the school. (3) <u>We wouldn't have to pay much to get there</u> and accommodation is included in the overall price.

(4) <u>You can do stuff like</u> canoeing, rock climbing and orienteering and the centre also organizes evening events such as sports competitions and games. (5) <u>We could have a real laugh</u> together in a very different atmosphere from that of the school.

Rington

(6) <u>Something that'd be a bit more relaxing</u>, and an ideal way to unwind after the exams, would be a trip to the seaside resort of Rington. Students could enjoy gentle walks on the coastal path, sunbathing on the beach and even a swim in the sea if the water is warm enough. (7) <u>There's loads to do in the evening</u>, including the numerous seafood restaurants for which the town is known.

Conclusion

(8) <u>Where we end up going</u> depends on how much students are willing to pay and whether they prefer an active or a more relaxing trip.

---

3 Choose a more formal alternative **a–h** for each of the sentence beginnings **1–8** in exercise **2** above.

Example: 1d

    a An inexpensive, yet very enjoyable option would be a weekend at

    b A rather more relaxing alternative

    c Activities include

    d The aim of this report is to

    e The final choice of destination

    f Students could have a great deal of fun

    g Rington also offers plenty of evening entertainment

    h Travel costs would be low

4 The question in exercise **1** asks you to 'explain why these places would be suitable for the trip'. What reasons does the writer of the answer in exercise **2** give for his/her two suggestions?

5 Now write your own answer to the question in exercise **1** on page 66.

> **Don't forget!**
>
> Write your report in a consistently formal style.
> Explain why your suggestions would be suitable.
> Give each section a heading.

Reading and Use of English
Part 6

Gapped text

1 You are going to read an article about a government report on UFOs. Six sentences have been removed from the article. Choose from the sentences **A–G** the one which fits each gap **(1–6)**. There is one extra sentence which you do not need to use.

Don't forget!

- Look for connections between the language in the text and the language in the missing sentences. To help you, key words and phrases have been underlined in the missing sentences.
- One of the sentences **A–G** is not required.

Just a load of hot air!

They **glow**, move across the sky at incredible speed and are invisible to radar. The mysterious shapes have for decades been **cited** by UFO enthusiasts as proof that we have attracted visitors from another world.

1 [ ] After four years of study they concluded that they are not flying saucers, but 'plasmas' of gas caused by charges of electricity in the atmosphere. The study by the Defence Intelligence Staff examined 30 years of apparent flying saucer sightings, which average about 100 a year.

Their 400-page report found that most of those who reported seeing UFOs – usually as glowing round or cigar-shaped objects – were not fantasists or hoaxers playing tricks. **2** [ ] The bright plasmas are created by charges of electricity. When air **flows** into them they are transformed into aerodynamic shapes which appear to fly at incredible speeds.

The electromagnetic fields can also cause responses in the brain, **tricking** observers into thinking they are seeing even more vivid impressions, the study found. Because they are electrically charged, plasmas can change shape or colour when **struck** by another energy source – such as radio signals sent out by UFO spotters. **3** [ ] The scientists concluded they now have 'a reasonably justified explanation' for the sightings that had previously been difficult to describe.

The aim of the study, codenamed Project Condign, was to assess any military threat from sightings of unexplained flying objects, many of which appeared to '**hover**, land, take off, accelerate to exceptional velocities and vanish'. The study was released under the Freedom of Information Act. Files previously released under this law showed that the Ministry of Defence maintained a special unit to **log** sightings of UFOs by the public and the military. **4** [ ] They described seeing 'bright objects hanging over the sea' around three miles from the coast at a height of around 5,000ft.

In July 1976, the captain of a British Airways Tri-Star on a return flight from Portugal told air traffic controllers of 'four objects – two round brilliant white, two cigar-shaped' 18 miles north of Faro. **5** [ ] A spokesman for the Ministry of Defence said: 'We have to check any report of an unidentified flying object to ensure it's not a threat. That's what this report was about. Once we are satisfied there is no threat, as this report concluded, we take no further action. We are not a UFO club.'

6 [ ] 'Even physicists studying plasma clouds do not fully understand them,' she said, 'so it is ridiculous for the Government to use a little known and poorly understood phenomenon as the main explanation for most UFO sightings.' She added: 'It may **account for** some, but by no means all. It does not explain incidents where ground trace evidence of UFOs has been left behind or where there is film footage of flying objects. The MoD will never release any documents that suggest there may be some mystery surrounding UFO sightings, but the simple fact is that some are mysterious.'

A These included a report by <u>Flight Lieutenant A M Wood and two non-commissioned officers</u> in Northumberland in July 1977.

B '<u>This</u> has led ufologists to <u>imagine</u> that an <u>alien response</u> is being given to <u>their signals</u>,' said the report.

C <u>Judy Jaafar</u>, secretary of the British UFO Research Association, <u>criticized the report</u>.

D Defence chiefs, <u>however</u>, have a rather <u>less exciting explanation</u> for the glowing objects in the sky.

E <u>However</u>, the <u>Government</u> seems to agree that <u>not all incidents such as these</u> can be <u>explained scientifically</u>.

F Fighter planes were sent to investigate and shortly afterwards the crew on <u>two other commercial flights</u> in <u>the same area</u> reported <u>similar sightings</u>.

G <u>They</u> were describing unusual but entirely <u>natural events</u> in the atmosphere.

2 Match the words in bold in the text with the meanings **a–h**. Use the context to help you. The meanings are in the infinitive form.

a hit

b deceive; make someone believe something which is not true

c be the explanation or cause of something

d produce a continuous light

e mention (in order to support a belief)

f record officially

g move continuously

h stay in the same place in the air

3 Complete the sentences with the correct form of the bold verbs in the text.

1 Believing the email – supposedly from Boyd's Bank – to be genuine, she was _____ into disclosing her credit card details.

2 Poor exam results were _____ as evidence of the failure of the Government's education policies.

3 The demonstration was monitored by two police helicopters _____ noisily overhead.

4 We saw a large, burnt-out tree which had probably been _____ by lightning.

5 Bad weather _____ 76 per cent of delays at UK airports last year.

6 They live next to a motorway, so a constant stream of traffic _____ past their house.

7 She knew he was still there: she could see his smartphone _____ in his pocket.

8 Before itemized telephone bills we had to _____ all personal calls from the office in a red notebook.

Vocabulary

Wordlist on page 208 of the Coursebook

A Ways of looking

Underline the correct alternative.

1 Lucy *gazed/glimpsed* in admiration at Tom in his smart new uniform.

2 Her eyes locked onto his and she *glared/glanced* at him with hatred and anger.

3 Jake *peered/stared* wide-eyed in horror at the cut on his arm.

4 I didn't see the prince very well – I just caught a brief *glimpse/peer* of him.

5 I haven't read the newspaper – I only had a quick *gaze/glance* at the front page.

6 Unable to control his curiosity, Alex *glared/peered* through the crack in the fence.

B Phrasal verbs with *give*

Phrasal verb list on pages 130–132

Match **1–7** to **a–g** to make logical sentences.

1 As soon as I **gave up**		**a** **state secrets**, he was arrested and held in jail.
2 The cooker was **giving off**		**b** **the homework** tomorrow morning.
3 Suspected of **giving away**		**c** **smoking**, I felt a lot better.
4 He listened closely as they **gave out**		**d** **food** to homeless people.
5 She said we had to **give in**		**e** **a strange smell**, so I got someone to look at it.
6 Street Aid is a charity which **gives out**		**f** **the money** I lent him until Friday.
7 He says he can't **give back**		**g** **the winning lottery numbers** on the news.

C Expressions with *give*

Lexical phrase list on pages 133–134

Complete the sentences with words from the box.

call   example   hand   idea   impression   lift   party   permission

1 'Risk' is a verb which takes the gerund. Can anyone give another _____ ?

2 Dave gave me a _____ to work in his new car this morning.

3 I can't move this table on my own. Can anyone give me a _____ ?

4 The manager has given me _____ to take two days off work.

5 He gave me the _____ that he was bored; he kept sighing during the lesson.

6 I won't be at home tomorrow, but can you give me a _____ on my mobile?

7 Would you give me some _____ of what time you'll be coming home, so I'll know when to have dinner ready?

8 Linda is thinking of giving a _____ to celebrate her husband's 40th birthday.

D Collocations

One adjective in each group is not normally used with the noun in capital letters. Underline the word which does not fit.

0	deep	impatient	<u>open-air</u>	loud	**SIGH**
1	piercing	loud	blank	high-pitched	**SCREAM**
2	tender	big	passionate	baggy	**KISS**
3	full	precise	nervous	relevant	**DETAILS**
4	lengthy	luxurious	impressive	boring	**SPEECH**
5	long-haul	tender	broad	friendly	**SMILE**
6	loud	spotty	nervous	cruel	**LAUGH**
7	sedentary	nasty	great	terrible	**SHOCK**
8	live	outstanding	convincing	curly	**PERFORMANCE**

E Word formation

1 Write the adjective and adverb forms of the nouns **1–10**.

Noun	Adjective	Adverb
0 noise	*noisy*	*noisily*
1 humour		
2 passion		
3 finance		
4 anger		
5 mystery		
6 nature		
7 success		
8 attraction		
9 enthusiasm		
10 offence		

2 Complete the sentences with the appropriate form of the words in capitals. You may need to write a negative form.

0 The children were playing _____*NOISILY*_____ and I couldn't think straight. **NOISE**

1 Seventy-eight-year-old Bill Baxter has _____ completed his third marathon. **SUCCESS**

2 I think it's an extremely _____ building; it's far too big and it ruins the character of the area. **ATTRACTION**

3 The former minister spoke _____ about the need for more investment in education. **PASSION**

4 When I was at school, history lessons were really boring; the teacher was so dull and _____ . **ENTHUSIASM**

5 Bees are not _____ aggressive and will sting only when threatened. **NATURE**

6 Our company is experiencing a few _____ problems. **FINANCE**

7 During the conversation, Paul suddenly and unexpectedly got up and stormed _____ out of the room. **ANGER**

8 I don't know why he got so annoyed; it was a completely _____ comment. **OFFENCE**

Language focus

 Grammar reference on pages 216–217 of the Coursebook

A Modal verbs of speculation

1 There is a mistake in five of the sentences below. Find the mistakes and rewrite the sentences so that they are correct.

1 I can't find my keys. I think I might leave them on my desk at work.

_____

2 The dog's barking a lot. He might be trying to tell us something.

_____

3 Sally's not answering the phone. She can have gone away for the weekend, or perhaps she's just gone to the shops.

_____

4 It's his birthday tomorrow, so he must be excited.

_____

5 They said they'd found out what was wrong with the washing machine, but they can't have done because it's still not working properly.

_____

6 A: Andrea never wears that blouse we bought her.

   B: Well, she might not like the colour, it may not go with her skirts or it could not be the right size. Who knows?

_____

7 Jim mustn't be going out with Sue; she's just got engaged to Doug.

_____

8 You've got nearly all the homework answers wrong. You couldn't have been paying attention in the lesson.

_____

9 It's a shame Mark hasn't come. He must decide to stay at home.

_____

10 The tennis rackets aren't in the car. You must have forgotten to put them in.

_____

2 Use modal verbs to write one or more explanations for the following situations.

0 He can't drive for two months.

He could have broken his leg or his wife might be using the car.

1 He looks exhausted.

2 She isn't eating very much at the moment.

3 There's a lot of traffic in the city centre today.

4 The plants have all died.

5 The police came to speak to the neighbours this morning.

6 John seems very happy these days.

B Question tags

Complete the sentences with an appropriate question tag.

1 He hasn't been here long, _____ ?

2 I'm getting old, _____ ?

3 He plays for Barcelona, _____ ?

4 You'd like to come, _____ ?

5 She said she was ill, _____ ?

6 Don't make too much noise, _____ ?

7 Help me lift this box, _____ ?

8 Let's go to the cinema, _____ ?

9 Nothing serious happened, _____ ?

10 No one lives here now, _____ ?

C Contrast linkers

Choose the most appropriate option, **A**, **B** or **C**. Sometimes more than one answer is possible.

1 I'm not keen on shopping for clothes, whereas

A my brother isn't either.

B my sister loves it.

C I'm not fond of shopping for food.

2 I often had rows with my brother.

   A However, we sometimes fell out.

   B However, we always remained good friends.

   C However, we never hit each other.

3 I enjoy living in the town centre, despite

   A the noise.

   B it's so noisy.

   C being so noisy.

4 Although we arrived late for the concert,

   A we missed the first few songs.

   B they wouldn't let us go in.

   C we managed to get a good seat.

5 We got on well when we shared a flat, in spite

   A of the difference in our ages.

   B of her being much older than me.

   C the fact I was much younger than her.

6 I'm glad I went to the sales, despite

   A the long wait in the cold.

   B of the fact the queue was so long.

   C having to wait so long in the cold.

Reading and Use of English
Part 1

Multiple-choice cloze

For questions **1–8**, read the text below and decide which answer (**A**, **B**, **C** or **D**) best fits each gap. There is an example at the beginning (**0**).

The wild man of China

Most people are (**0**) _____ with the yeti, a large hairy man-like creature, which is (**1**) _____ to live in the Himalayas. (**2**) _____ , you might not have heard of the *yeren* or 'wild man' of China, which was mentioned and drawn for the first time more than 2,000 years ago. In recent decades there have been over 200 (**3**) _____ of the *yeren* in the Shennongjia Nature Reserve in central Hubei province.

Those who claim to have (**4**) _____ a glimpse of it have described it as approximately 1.6 metres tall, with long red hair, rounded eyes and a broad forehead. It also seems (**5**) _____ of an incredible range of calls and noises. When disturbed, it is said to sound like a dog, a wolf, a donkey and even a crying child.

Some years ago a Chinese scientist (**6**) _____ up in a gorilla costume and entered a forest in the (**7**) _____ of getting a closer look at a *yeren*. Not surprisingly he failed, as have so many others who have gone in (**8**) _____ of this elusive creature.

0 A aware	**B** conscious	**C** <u>familiar</u>	**D** known
1 A reported	**B** informed	**C** noticed	**D** announced
2 A Actually	**B** Instead	**C** However	**D** Moreover
3 A views	**B** visions	**C** looks	**D** sightings
4 A caught	**B** found	**C** appeared	**D** watched
5 A able	**B** competent	**C** capable	**D** powerful
6 A wore	**B** dressed	**C** put	**D** changed
7 A attempt	**B** hope	**C** order	**D** wish
8 A search	**B** look	**C** hunt	**D** sight

Open cloze

For questions **1–8**, read the text below and think of the word which best fits each gap. Use only **one** word in each gap. There is an example at the beginning **(0)**. Write your answers **IN CAPITAL LETTERS**.

Bad luck superstitions

There are several superstitions **(0)** *WHICH* are common to a number of different cultures, and most of these have their origins in the distant past. Spilling salt, for example, is considered in many countries **(1)** _____ bring bad luck. One reason for this is to do **(2)** _____ cost; for many hundreds of years, salt was a precious resource, difficult to extract and, **(3)** _____ a result, very expensive. Not only was it a valuable preservative, **(4)** _____ it was also linked with health and a long life, so spilling salt would have **(5)** _____ seen as both wasteful and a threat to longevity.

Another superstition says that breaking a mirror will bring seven years' bad luck. Apparently, the Romans are responsible **(6)** _____ this one, since they believed that a person's reflection in a mirror represented their soul, so damaging a mirror corrupted the soul of the person that broke **(7)** _____ . They also believed that the soul renewed itself every seven years, so the soul would **(8)** _____ be restored until the next seven-year period had passed.

Essay

1 Read the following Part 1 instructions.

In your English class you have been talking about how best to spend local authority money. Now, your English teacher has asked you to write an essay.

Write an essay using all the notes and give reasons for your point of view.

Essay question

It is better for local authorities to spend money on museums rather than libraries. Do you agree?

Notes

Write about:

1 which are more important to us

2 which need the money more

3 .... (your own idea)

Write your **essay** in **140–190** words. You must use grammatically correct sentences with accurate spelling and punctuation in a style appropriate for the situation.

2a Read the model essay below and answer these questions.

1 Is the style formal or informal?

2 Is it appropriate for the situation?

b Read the model essay again and complete the essay with words from the box.

conclude	hand	invest	more	opinion
result	pay	spend	too	whereas

In recent years museums have become more interactive, and as a **(1)** _____ , attract more visitors. The number of adults entering libraries, on the other **(2)** _____ , has fallen, as e-book readers have become more popular. Which of these two places should local authorities **(3)** _____ more money in?

Certainly, museums are important to us as places to store objects which tell us about our past. Libraries **(4)** _____ , though, are places where knowledge is kept for future generations, in a world where information-storage devices and formats are constantly changing.

However, museums can raise money by charging entrance fees, **(5)** _____
libraries provide free access to Internet services and books to families who
cannot afford to buy them. In my **(6)** _____ , therefore, libraries are
more in need of local authority money than museums.

What is **(7)** _____ , investment in libraries would increase the number
of visitors by enabling them to become dynamic and interactive like museums.
Libraries could use the money to **(8)** _____ for talks by authors or
storytellers, and organize other cultural activities, such as workshops for
children.

To **(9)** _____ , local authorities should **(10)** _____ more money on
libraries to help them become as popular as museums.

3 What point does the writer make for 'your own idea', number **3** in the Notes section in
exercise **1** on page 74?

4 Underline the linking words and expressions the writer uses in the model essay in **2b**
on pages 74–75.
… <u>and as a result</u>, attract more visitors.

5 Write an answer to one of the following questions, **A** or **B**.

A In your English class you have been talking about the advantages and disadvantages of
using tablets rather than books in the classroom. Now, your English teacher has asked
you to write an essay.

Write an essay using **all** the notes and give
reasons for your point of view.

Write your **essay** in **140–190** words.

B In your English class you have been talking
about the best ways for governments to
spend money. Now, your English teacher has
asked you to write an essay.

Write an essay using **all** the notes and give
reasons for your point of view.

Write your **essay** in **140–190** words.

Essay question
t is better for schools to spend money on
tablets for their students rather than books.
Do you agree?

Notes
Write about:
1 effect on student concentration
2 cost of repair or replacement
3 .... (your own idea)

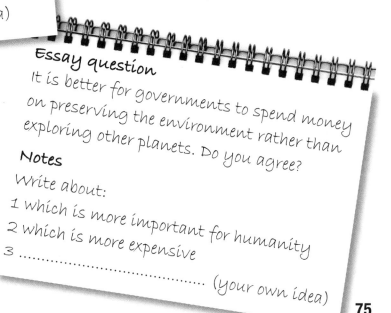

Essay question
It is better for governments to spend money
on preserving the environment rather than
exploring other planets. Do you agree?
Notes
Write about:
1 which is more important for humanity
2 which is more expensive
3 .... (your own idea)

Multiple matching

1 You are going to read an article about techniques used by thieves. For questions **1–10**, choose from the people **(A–D)**. The people may be chosen more than once.

- **A** Steve Sheppardson
- **B** David Shamash
- **C** Ita Kelly
- **D** Barry Sheppard

Which of the people suggests the following?

I was shortly going to be leaving the city.	**1**
I was unable to chase the thieves as they fled.	**2**
It made me suspicious for the rest of my visit.	**3**
I had problems understanding them.	**4**
I took action to avoid being robbed.	**5**
I was not the first person to be tricked in this way.	**6**
My actions made it obvious I was not a local.	**7**
I gave a small reward.	**8**
Something which smelled bad was used to create confusion.	**9**
I only discovered I had been robbed several hours later.	**10**

Travellers' tales

Hanging on to your money

When I reported that three men recently attempted to rob me at Krakow bus station, several readers got in touch with their own stories.

Steve Sheppardson reports an experience in Manhattan: 'We were sitting on a park bench and I was carrying a large camera bag over my shoulder. When a group of teenagers ran past and around us,
5 I held tightly on to the camera thinking this might be more than just youngsters having fun.

'Five minutes later, somebody pointed to the back of my jacket and held their nose – when I took off the jacket, the back was covered in a wet, sticky
10 substance with an unpleasant odour. At this point we got lucky – a shop assistant came out, invited us in to clean up and told us what had happened: the kids we saw had squirted my back with something like washing-up liquid that sticks and makes a mess.
15 In the confusion, many people put their bag down to take their jacket off and the bag is snatched when they are least expecting it.'

This account comes from **David Shamash**: 'I was driving into Barcelona recently when the car in front
20 stalled at the lights when they went green – the driver got out and in the confusion (as I soon found out) knifed my back tyre. Naturally I pulled over to investigate the puncture and in the few seconds I was out of the car my bag was stolen. By the time

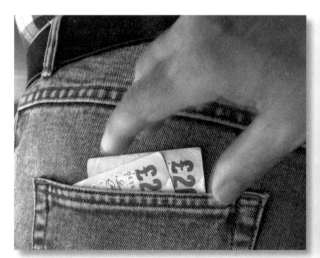

25 I realized this, they had driven off in their car and I was completely helpless. The police informed me that it was a common technique.'

And **Ita Kelly** reports an incident that occurred on a visit to Madrid: 'I made the mistake one morning
30 of looking at a tourist map just near the entrance to the Plaza Mayor. A few minutes later a young man walked towards me and dropped some coins at my feet. As I helped him pick them up, a pickpocket

took my wallet which was inside my buttoned-
35 up back pocket. All this happened in the space of
seconds and I didn't feel a thing. Not until I got
back to my hotel in the evening did I realize what
had happened. Luckily I had left my credit cards in
the hotel so I didn't suffer too much inconvenience,
40 but I was left feeling angry and paranoid for what
remained of my stay.'

Barry Sheppard tells of an incident in Italy: 'I was
in Florence and preparing to move to Venice. I had
been to the station to check the train times for
45 the next day and was walking back towards my
hotel when two women approached and pushed a
newspaper under my eyes. They spoke quickly and
excitedly, pointing violently at a photograph in the
paper; I had no idea what they were on about so I
50 just smiled and moved on. A sixth sense made me
feel for my wallet, which, of course, was gone.

'Naturally, the women had disappeared, but a man
was hurrying towards me waving my wallet! He
turned out to be a local who had seen what was
55 happening and had managed to snatch the wallet
back from them. All it cost me was a Campari and
soda.'

2 Match the words from the text **1–6** to the meanings **a–f**. The line numbers are given in brackets.

1 pointed (7)		**a**	drew attention to something by holding out a finger
2 squirted (13)		**b**	taken quickly
3 sticks (14)		**c**	covered with a liquid (from a tube or similar)
4 snatched (16)		**d**	moving the hand from side to side
5 stalled (20)		**e**	becomes attached
6 waving (53)		**f**	stopped working

3 Complete the sentences with the correct form of the words from exercise **2**.
  1 As she walked out of the hotel, a man _____ her bag from her and ran off.
  2 We used to use an old washing-up liquid bottle to _____ water at each other.
  3 She was shouting excitedly, _____ her certificate in the air.
  4 During my driving test my car _____ on a hill and I started rolling backwards.
  5 She sat on some chewing gum and it _____ to her jeans.
  6 He _____ at the door and told me to get out of his office.

4 Complete the extracts from the text **1–5** with the correct form of verbs from the box. The verbs are the same for **a** and **b**.

get	have	hold	leave	make	~~take~~

  0 a In the confusion, many people put their bag down to _*take*_ their jacket off …
    b As I helped him pick them up, a pickpocket _*took*_ my wallet …
  1 a When a group of teenagers ran past and around us, I _____ tightly on to the camera.
    b Five minutes later, somebody pointed to the back of my jacket and _____ their nose …
  2 a … something like washing-up liquid that sticks and _____ a mess.
    b I _____ the mistake one morning of looking at a tourist map …
  3 a … several readers _____ in touch with their own stories.
    b Not until I _____ back to my hotel in the evening did I realize what had happened.
  4 a Luckily I had _____ my credit cards in the hotel …
    b … I was _____ feeling angry and paranoid for what remained of my stay.
  5 a … thinking this might be more than just youngsters _____ fun.
    b I _____ no idea what they were on about so I just smiled and moved on.

Vocabulary

Wordlist on page 208 of the Coursebook

A Crime and punishment

1 Match the crimes in the box to descriptions **1–5**.

arson	blackmail	burglary	kidnap	~~pickpocketing~~	robbery

0 By the time he realized his wallet was missing, it was too late. The bus had stopped and the two men had run off in different directions. _pickpocketing_

1 Police believe the building may have been burned down by an ex-employee who was sacked from the company three months ago. _____

2 Three armed men, each wearing a stocking over his head, ordered the customers to lie still on the floor while the cashier emptied the safe. _____

3 We must have left a window open. They took both computers, the television and all my jewellery. The neighbours didn't hear a thing. _____

4 Mrs Brandon received a note demanding £1 million in return for the release of her husband. _____

5 He was demanding regular monthly payments of £3,000 in return for his silence over the politician's affair with his secretary. _____

2 Complete the text with the correct form of verbs from the box.

acquit	give	order	sentence

The victims were hoping that all three men would be **(1)** _____ to at least ten years in prison. However, Brent was the only one to be **(2)** _____ a prison sentence and he will be behind bars for a maximum of five years. Taylor was **(3)** _____ to pay a fine of £3,000 and do 300 hours of community service, while Jackson was **(4)** _____ of all charges and released.

B Paraphrasing

Complete each gap with a preposition. The sentence pairs have the same meaning.

1 It could cost thousands to repair.   Repair costs could run _____ thousands.

2 The plan isn't at all perfect.   The plan is far _____ perfect.

3 Lara's a very good tennis player.   Lara's very good _____ playing tennis.

4 We couldn't see anybody.   There was nobody _____ sight.

5 Paul went to the concert alone.   Paul went to the concert _____ his own.

6 You aren't the only intelligent one.   You don't have a monopoly _____ intelligence.

C Phrasal verbs

Phrasal verb list on pages 130–132

1 Complete each pair of sentences with words from the box. The words are the same for **a** and **b**.

out of	out with	up with	up to

1 a The chair had been smashed to pieces, but no one owned _____ breaking it.

b I look _____ my dad; I admire the way he has made a success of his life.

2 a I'm trying to come _____ a plan to get rich, but nothing legal occurs to me.

b Eli's split _____ Jim; she couldn't put _____ his arrogance any longer.

3 a Joey's parents finally ran _____ patience and threw him out of the house.

b She tried to get _____ paying the speeding fine by claiming she had been rushing her sick mother to hospital.

4 a Paul and Sue have been going _____ each other for three years now.

b Lucy fell _____ her mum on her birthday and hasn't spoken to her since.

2 Complete the sentences with the correct form of verbs from the box.

give	nod	show	take	tell

1 The teacher _____ me off for shouting and made me stay in during breaktime.
2 I kept _____ off during the film, it was so boring.
3 The hairdryer was _____ off a smell of burning so I stopped using it.
4 I wish you'd stop _____ off about how well you can speak German.
5 His music career _____ off after he won a television talent show.

Language focus

 Grammar reference on page 217 of the Coursebook

A Active and passive

Complete the sentences with an appropriate active or passive form of the verb in brackets. You may need to use more than one word in each gap.

1 Glenn Lambert _____ (release) from prison yesterday, ten years after _____ (find) guilty of a crime he _____ (not commit).
2 Our car _____ (repair) at the garage at the moment. I _____ (tell) yesterday that it probably _____ (not be) ready until next Friday.
3 **A:** I _____ (ask) to give a talk at the conference next month.
   B: So have I. I _____ (not prepare) mine yet. How about you?
4 **A:** What _____ (happen) to those boys who _____ (catch) spraying paint on the walls of the school last year?
   B: Don't you remember? They _____ (make) to clean it all off. It _____ (take) them three days altogether.
5 Three million chocolate bars _____ (produce) at this factory each week. Over one million of these _____ (sell) in the UK, and the rest _____ (export) to other European countries.
6 My great grandfather _____ (give) a beautiful clock when he retired in 1960. When he _____ (die) in 1980, the clock _____ (stop) working; it still _____ (not fix).
7 A Roman necklace, which _____ (think) to be worth over £2 million, _____ (find) last week by Audrey Perham while she _____ (walk) her dog in Queen's Park, Brighton.
8 There were two of them, both about ten years old. They came into my garden and _____ (destroy) all the flowers. The police still _____ (not do) anything about it. It's not right – they shouldn't _____ (allow) to get away with it!

B Passive of reporting verbs

Rewrite the sentences beginning with the underlined words.

0 They do not believe that <u>the escaped prisoner</u> is dangerous.
   The escaped prisoner is not believed to be dangerous.

1 Police know that <u>the family</u> runs a number of illegal businesses.
2 They think that <u>Smith</u> broke into several homes.
3 Everyone expects <u>she</u> will be given a life sentence.
4 They say that <u>Robinson</u> is enjoying prison life.
5 It is considered that <u>Corelli</u> was the mastermind behind the crime.

Multiple-choice cloze

For questions **1–8**, read the text below and decide which answer (**A**, **B**, **C** or **D**) best fits each gap. There is an example at the beginning (**0**).

A novel programme

Inmates in four federal prisons (**0**) ____ some of Brazil's most notorious criminals will be able to read up to 12 (**1**) ____ of literature, philosophy, science or classics to trim a maximum 48 days off their (**2**) ____ each year, the government announced.

Prisoners will have up to four weeks to read each book and write an essay which must '(**3**) ____ correct use of paragraphs, be (**4**) ____ of corrections, use margins and legible joined-up (**5**) ____ ,' said the notice published in the official gazette. A special panel will decide which inmates are eligible to (**6**) ____ in the programme entitled 'Redemption through Reading'. 'A person can (**7**) ____ prison more enlightened and with an enlarged vision of the world,' said Sao Paulo lawyer Andre Kehdi, who (**8**) ____ a book donation project for prisons.

0 A staying	**B** locking	**C** <u>holding</u>	**D** dealing
1 A pieces	**B** works	**C** parts	**D** sections
2 A arrest	**B** sentence	**C** capture	**D** fine
3 A take	**B** put	**C** give	**D** make
4 A free	**B** loose	**C** empty	**D** lack
5 A word	**B** letter	**C** lyric	**D** writing
6 A involve	**B** occupy	**C** participate	**D** include
7 A release	**B** leave	**C** liberate	**D** outcome
8 A charges	**B** rules	**C** heads	**D** gains

Open cloze

For questions **1–8**, read the text below and think of the word which best fits each gap. Use only **one** word in each gap. There is an example at the beginning (**0**). Write your answers **IN CAPITAL LETTERS**.

House-sitters

Nowadays (**0**) _THERE_ are far too many stories of homeowners who have been away on holiday and come home to find that their house has been broken (**1**) _____ . Unfortunately, simply locking the doors and cancelling the newspapers is (**2**) _____ enough to keep out burglars.

A much better way to prevent your home from (**3**) _____ burgled is to employ a professional house-sitter, either through an agency (**4**) _____ by placing an advertisement in a magazine. House-sitters are paid a daily rate (**5**) _____ around £20, including a food allowance, to live in a house while the owners are away. An extra charge is made if the house-sitter is required to (**6**) _____ care of one or more pets.

Agencies, which charge a considerable fee for their services, accept full responsibility (**7**) _____ anything which might go wrong. House-sitters are therefore chosen very carefully; as (**8**) _____ as the usual interview and personal references, inquiries are made about any previous criminal convictions.

Word formation

For questions **1–8**, read the text below. Use the word given in capitals at the end of some of the lines to form a word that fits in the gap in the same line. There is an example at the beginning **(0)**. Write your answers **IN CAPITAL LETTERS**.

CCTV cameras

Closed-circuit television cameras are a fact of life in modern Britain.
They can be seen in office **(0)** _BUILDINGS_ , shopping centres,   **BUILD**
banks, **(1)** _____ areas and even parks, and it is estimated   **RESIDENT**
that the average Briton is filmed over 300 times a day. It is believed
that CCTV leads to a **(2)** _____ in certain types of crime,   **REDUCE**
such as car theft, **(3)** _____ and street violence. Its   **ROB**
supporters defend it as an **(4)** _____ way of improving   **EFFECT**
security in town centres, and of helping to bring **(5)** _____   **CRIME**
to justice. Civil liberties groups, who object to the **(6)** _____   **PRESENT**
of the cameras, feel that they constitute a serious **(7)** _____   **INVADE**
of privacy and say that there is little **(8)** _____ that they   **EVIDENT**
reduce offending.

Transformations

For questions **1–6**, complete the second sentence so that it has a similar meaning to the first sentence, using the word given. **Do not change the word given.** You must use between **two** and **five** words, including the word given.

1 He's too short to be a good goalkeeper.
   ENOUGH
   He's _____ a good goalkeeper.

2 I couldn't concentrate because it was too noisy.
   TOO
   I couldn't concentrate because _____ noise.

3 They made him eat alone in the kitchen.
   MADE
   He _____ his own in the kitchen.

4 The problem is being dealt with at this very moment.
   SORTED
   The problem _____ at this very moment.

5 The witness had invented the whole story.
   MADE
   The whole story had _____ the witness.

6 People say swimming is good exercise for your back.
   SAID
   Swimming _____ good exercise for your back.

Informal email

1 Read the following Part 2 instructions and the two answers which were written by students. Which email do you think would be given a higher mark?

You have just returned from a holiday abroad, during which something of yours was stolen. Write an email to your penfriend, telling him/her about the incident and what you did to try to recover the stolen item.

Write your **email** in **140–190** words.

Student A

Dear Paul

I arrive to the station to caught the train to the airport. I feeling sad because of I finish my holiday. I enjoyed with the holiday very much and I didn't want to come to home.

I have decided to go to the shop for to buy some sweets and make me felt happier. I put my suitcase to the ground and paid to the woman for the sweets. I wanted to pick up my suitcase but it was not there anymore! Where was my suitcase? What a shock! Somebody stealed it.

Consequently, I feeling sadder. It was a horrible way to finish of a holiday.

Helmut Braun

Student B

Dear Esther

How are you? Did you get my postcard from Italy? You'll never guess what happened to me after I'd posted it to you!

I was walking down the main street on my way to the beach when I heard everyone shouting behind me. I looked round and there on the pavement coming towards me was a young man on a motor scooter. Before I knew what was happening, he had snatched my bag and was riding off into the distance.

I started to run after him but it was useless – you know how unfit I am! Anyway, at that moment a car pulled over beside me and the driver, who had seen the incident, told me to get in. We chased after the thief, and as soon as he realized he was being followed, he dropped the bag and disappeared.

You can imagine how relieved I felt. And I was so grateful to the driver – thanks to him my holiday wasn't ruined.

How about you, Esther? Did anything exciting happen on your holiday? Write and tell me all about it.

Lots of love

Angela

A Analysis

Read the two emails again and answer Yes or No to the following questions.

	A	B
Content		
1 Has the writer answered all parts of the question?		
2 Would the reader understand what happened and know what the writer did to try to recover the stolen item?		
Organization		
3 Is the email organized into suitable paragraphs?		
4 Are ideas connected with appropriate linking words?		
5 Does the email have an appropriate beginning and ending?		
Language		
6 Is there a good range of vocabulary?		
7 Has the writer used a variety of tenses?		
8 Is the English reasonably accurate?		
Style and format		
9 Is the email written in an informal style?		
10 Is the answer clearly set out as an email?		

B Accuracy

Look back at Student A's answer. Find the following mistakes and correct them.

1 eight mistakes related to verb forms, e.g. *I arrived*
2 eight mistakes related to the incorrect use of prepositions, e.g. *at the station*

C Addressing the reader

Look back at Student B's answer. Underline sentences in which the writer talks directly to the reader of the email.

<u>How are you?</u>

D Writing task

Now write your own answer to the question.

> **Don't forget!**
>
> - Set your answer out as an informal email.
> - Include suitable opening and closing paragraphs.
> - See pages 14–15 in Unit 1 of the Coursebook for useful language.
> - Use a range of vocabulary and structures when describing what happened.
> - Organize your ideas into logical paragraphs.
> - You could have one paragraph to describe how the item was stolen and another to say how you tried to recover it.

Gapped text

1 You are going to read a newspaper article about a shop that does not provide packaging. Six sentences have been removed from the article. Choose from the sentences **A–G** the one which fits each gap **1–6**. There is one extra sentence which you do not need to use.

Unpackaged

It sells everything you could ever need for a great meal. There's only one catch – it won't give you anything to take it all home in.

If you ever catch yourself looking at the kitchen bin guiltily, with its huge pile of plastic packets, cardboard containers and wrappers, you might be interested to know there's a whole movement that aims to go one better than even recycling: precycling, or cutting out packaging in the first place.

Among those at the forefront of this consumer revolution is Unpackaged, a first-of-its-kind shop that avoids all packaging and invites you to provide your own containers to stock up on essentials such as flour, cereals, nuts, pasta, rice and lentils. **1** Simply weigh your container when you arrive so it can be deducted from the overall weight and then get filling. Not only will you save money, but by foregoing packaging you'll reduce the amount of material waste being either sent to landfills or incinerated.

In its large store in Hackney, East London, Unpackaged offers a wide range of products, as well as a bar and café, run by Kate de Syllas, a well-known local chef. **2** She started out doing market stalls specializing in eco products and a small range of wholefoods and nuts. 'I wanted to see how people reacted. Would they bring their own containers and refill?' Conway says. 'It did really well and we ended up with two market stalls, but it was a bit impractical lugging all the stuff around.'

The company has a clear philosophy that includes sourcing organic, fair-trade products where possible, supporting artisan local producers and applying the principles of 'reduce, reuse, recycle' to all parts of its operation. **3** As well as using unsold produce in the café, it uses black tiles with erasable white wax pencils instead of printing off labels for products.

It even has a solution for that most eco-unfriendly product, the takeaway paper coffee cup, with its 'The 1000 Cup Countdown' scheme. Unpackaged has promised to provide 1000 biodegradable cups, each of which comes complete with an RFID (radio frequency identification) tag that will tell you more about the company's aims and if returned, will earn you a free coffee. **4**

'We want to be the local store,' Conway says. 'We want them to come here rather than go to a supermarket.' **5** But at the moment Unpackaged finds its dedicated customers are travelling from all over. 'They're coming for the atmosphere as much as what we're trying to do.'

an RFID tag

6 'The whole point is to take people on a journey with you,' Conway says. 'If someone comes in and they're not green and they don't have any containers, I don't want to say that I won't serve them, because they go away with such an awful view of what we do. Whereas if we say that this time we'll provide them with a small paper bag and next time they can bring their own, then it takes them two or three goes and they'll end up bringing their own.'

A This commitment to reducing waste and packaging is present in every aspect of the store.

B With the larger space it can now offer a greater range of products.

C When it runs out of them, customers will provide their own takeaway mug or sit in for their morning cappuccino.

D But what if someone new to the values of the store wanders in looking for some pasta?

E Bring bottles for oils, apple juice, wine and even gin.

F She hopes to spend more time developing an own line of Unpackaged products and she also hopes to set up other branches around London.

G It was founded by Catherine Conway, who got the idea while pouring rice from a plastic packet into a jar at home.

2 a Complete each pair of sentences with the correct form of words from the box. The words are the same for **a** and **b**.

catch	come	~~do~~	go	run

0 a 'It ___did___ **really well** and we ended up with two market stalls ...'

   b 'They're coming for the atmosphere as much as what we're trying to ___do___ .'

1 a ... there's a whole movement that **aims to** _____ **one better than** recycling.

   b ... **it takes them two or three** _____ and they'll end up bringing their own.

2 a Unpackaged has promised to provide 1000 biodegradable cups, each of which _____ **complete with** an RFID tag ...

   b 'We want them to _____ here rather than go to a supermarket.'

3 a Unpackaged offers ... a bar and café, _____ by Kate de Syllas ...

   b When **it** _____ **out of them**, customers will provide their own takeaway mug or sit in for their morning cappuccino.

4 a **There's only one** _____ – it won't give you anything to take it all home in.

   b If you ever _____ yourself looking at the kitchen bin guiltily ...

b Match the meanings **1–5** to the expressions in bold in exercise **2a**.

0 it was very successful   ___it did really well___

1 includes   _____

2 there are none left   _____

3 tries to improve on   _____

4 there's just one problem   _____

5 they need two or three attempts _____

Vocabulary

Wordlist on page 208 of the Coursebook

A The environment

1 Match **1–6** to **a–f** to make logical sentences.

1 One of the aims of Greenpeace is to **raise**

2 I strongly believe that anyone caught **dropping**

3 The ship's captain denied he had been **dumping**

4 Several species of birds and animals **face**

5 The local authorities talk of the need to **recycle**

6 Not enough is being done to **preserve**

a **extinction** in this country as a result of modern farming methods.

b **paper**, but they have not provided enough containers to enable us to do this.

c **awareness** of the environmental problems facing our planet.

d **litter** should be ordered to pay a heavy fine.

e **wildlife** in this country.

f **waste** of any kind at sea.

2   Match **1–7** to **a–g** to form compound nouns.

1 bottle	**a** effect
2 dog	**b** pollution
3 greenhouse	**c** mess
4 oil	**d** bank
5 sea	**e** slick
6 exhaust	**f** station
7 power	**g** fumes

3   Complete the sentences with compound nouns from exercise **2**.

1 _____ are responsible for a great deal of the pollution in our cities.

2 The huge _____ is moving slowly towards Ireland, and several miles of coastline are under threat.

3 It's almost impossible to walk on the pavement in this city without stepping in _____ .

4 Global warming is caused by the _____ , the result of an increase in the amount of carbon dioxide and other gases in the Earth's atmosphere.

5 Environmentalists have been protesting at the construction of a new nuclear _____ on the outskirts of the city.

B   The weather

Complete the crossword using the following clues.

Across

1 a long period of time without rain

6 a large amount of water covering an area which is normally dry

7 a very strong wind

8 a _____ storm is a very bad one

9 a _____ sea has lots of small waves caused by the wind

11 _____ rain consists of very small raindrops

12 'Several trees were _____ by lightning during the storm.'

13 a _____ is a short, sudden period of strong wind

Down

2 small hard balls of frozen rain

3 'Look at those thick, black _____ – I think it's going to rain.'

4 'After the earthquake came a _____ wave, which destroyed several houses on the coast.'

5 a gentle _____ is a very light wind

6 'You can't always rely on the weather _____ to predict the weather accurately.'

10 'to _____ with rain' means 'to rain very heavily'

C Lexical phrases: revision

Lexical phrase list on pages 133–134

Complete the sentences with the correct form of verbs from the box. Use each verb twice.

	get	give	put	take

1 This is the first time I _____ **my feet up** all day!
2 Would you mind _____ **care of** our plants while we're on holiday?
3 I hope they don't make me _____ **a speech** at the Christmas dinner.
4 If I had Alana's email address, I _____ **in touch with** her.
5 **Pressure** _____ **on** the minister to resign once the scandal became public.
6 It's unusual for Paul _____ **an interest in** sport, but he's mad about squash.
7 Now that we have children, we rarely _____ **the chance** to go to the theatre.
8 She read his letter, _____ **a deep sigh** then tore it up and threw it in the bin.

Language focus

 Grammar reference on pages 217–218 of the Coursebook

A *So*, *neither* and *nor*

1 Match the statements **1–8** to the replies **a–h**.

1 She doesn't like that type of music.	**a** So would I.
2 We didn't enjoy the film.	**b** I'm not.
3 I went swimming last night.	**c** Tim does.
4 My favourite food is pasta.	**d** So did my brother.
5 She's never been abroad.	**e** Neither did they.
6 I'd rather go to the cinema.	**f** We don't.
7 He's going to the demonstration.	**g** Neither have I.
8 I have to do a lot of homework tonight.	**h** So is mine.

2 Complete the sentences with *so*, *neither* or *nor* and an appropriate auxiliary verb.

0 He can't drive and ___*neither can*___ I.
1 I'm older than Harry, and _____ Stuart.
2 He never writes to me, and _____ Kate.
3 Her parents are going to France, and _____ mine.
4 Seamus came to the party, and _____ Patrick.
5 Hermione won't tell anyone, and _____ I.
6 I've already seen that film, and _____ Elisa.
7 I wouldn't be happy if you went alone, and _____ your father.
8 I'd better go to bed, and _____ you, young man.

B Conditionals

1 Complete the sentences with the correct form of the verb in brackets.

0 If I _____*had*_____ (have) more time, I _____*would help*_____ (help) you, but I'm afraid I'm just too busy.

1 I _____ (buy) you a new pair of football boots as long as you _____ (promise) to look after them properly.

2 Why did you tell your parents? If you _____ (not/say) anything, we _____ (not/get) into trouble.

3 If he _____ (sleep) for less than eight hours, he _____ (usually/be) bad-tempered all morning.

4 It's a shame you weren't at the party. If you _____ (go), you _____ (meet) my sister.

5 We _____ (finish) top of the league this season, providing we _____ (win) at least one of the last two games.

6 There's a quicker way to do it. If you _____ (press) 'Control' and 'U', it _____ (underline) your work as you type.

7 If I _____ (be) you, I _____ (go) to the doctor's.

8 We _____ (be) there by 6 o'clock this evening unless we _____ (get) stuck in a traffic jam.

9 If we _____ (stop) that taxi earlier, we _____ (be) at home by now.

2 Rewrite the sentences to form second, third or mixed conditional sentences.

0 I don't have to pay to get into the museum because I'm unemployed.
_____*If I wasn't unemployed, I'd have to pay to get into the museum.*_____

1 We didn't go sailing because there wasn't enough wind.
_____

2 We don't go abroad on holiday because I'm afraid of flying.
_____

3 He's broken his leg so he can't drive.
_____

4 I couldn't take any photos because I forgot to pack my camera.
_____

5 He isn't going to the wedding because he hasn't got a suit.
_____

6 He's feeling ill because he ate too much last night.
_____

7 She didn't pass her exams so she couldn't go to university.
_____

8 They didn't watch the news so they didn't hear about the earthquake.
_____

3 Complete the sentences in an appropriate way.

1 If I had to spend a year living abroad, I _____ .

2 If I had the power to change one thing in my country, I _____ .

3 I probably wouldn't have met my best friend if _____ .

4 I'd be really pleased if _____ .

5 I'll pass the *First* exam, providing _____ .

6 If the computer hadn't been invented, _____ .

Multiple-choice cloze

For questions **1–8**, read the text below and decide which answer (**A**, **B**, **C** or **D**) best fits each gap. There is an example at the beginning (**0**).

Global warming

Few people now (**0**) _____ the reality of global warming and its effects on the world's climate. Many scientists (**1**) _____ the blame for recent natural disasters on the increase in the world's temperature and are convinced that, more than ever before, the Earth is at (**2**) _____ from the forces of the wind, rain and sun. According to them, global warming is making extreme weather events, such as hurricanes and droughts, even more (**3**) _____ and causing sea levels all around the world to (**4**) _____ .

Environmental groups are putting (**5**) _____ on governments to take action to reduce the amount of carbon dioxide which is given (**6**) _____ by factories and power plants, thus attacking the problem at its source. They are in favour of more money being spent on research into solar, wind and wave energy devices.

Some scientists, (**7**) _____ , believe that even if we stopped releasing carbon dioxide and other gases into the atmosphere tomorrow, we would have to wait (**8**) _____ hundred years to notice the results.

0 A hesitate	**B** <u>question</u>	**C** disagree	**D** concern
1 A give	**B** put	**C** take	**D** have
2 A threat	**B** danger	**C** risk	**D** harm
3 A strict	**B** severe	**C** strong	**D** heavy
4 A lift	**B** arise	**C** raise	**D** rise
5 A force	**B** pressure	**C** persuasion	**D** encouragement
6 A off	**B** away	**C** up	**D** over
7 A whereas	**B** although	**C** despite	**D** however
8 A several	**B** over	**C** numerous	**D** various

Open cloze

For questions **1–8**, read the text below and think of the word which best fits each gap. Use only **one** word in each gap. There is an example at the beginning (**0**). Write your answers **IN CAPITAL LETTERS**.

Light pollution

When you gaze up into the sky at night, (**0**) __*HOW*__ clearly can you see the stars? According to the British Astronomical Association (BAA), less than 10 per cent of the UK population are fortunate enough (**1**) _____ observe a clear night sky. For the rest, it is obscured by light from artificial sources (**2**) _____ as neon advertising signs, car headlamps and street lighting, which throws as much light upwards (**3**) _____ it does downwards.

This is (**4**) _____ is known as 'light pollution', huge amounts of light shone wastefully into the sky, squandering resources and making it difficult (**5**) _____ us to appreciate the full beauty of the stars. The BAA's Campaign for Dark Skies aims to preserve and restore that beauty '(**6**) _____ campaigning against excessive, inefficient and irresponsible lighting that shines where it is (**7**) _____ wanted nor needed.'

The light from some of the stars in our galaxy takes thousands of years to reach our eyes. It seems a shame not to be able to welcome it (**8**) _____ the end of its long journey.

Transformations

For questions **1–6**, complete the second sentence so that it has a similar meaning to the first sentence, using the word given. **Do not change the word given.** You must use between **two** and **five** words, including the word given.

1 They have postponed the concert until September.

PUT

The concert _____ until September.

2 We'll play badminton later unless it's windy.

LONG

We'll play badminton later as _____ any wind.

3 Simon missed the early train because he overslept.

NOT

If Simon had _____ caught the early train.

4 We've had some heavy rain recently.

RAINING

It _____ recently.

5 Christina and Fiona both had a good time.

SO

Christina enjoyed _____ Fiona.

6 You need to spend longer on your homework.

MORE

You need to put _____ your homework.

Article

1 Read the following Part 2 instructions and the model answer below.

You see this announcement in an international magazine:

Write your **article** in **140–190** words.

WRITING COMPETITION

The best and the worst

The theme of our writing competition this month is **the weather**.

Write an article about your favourite and least favourite weather conditions, telling our readers why you feel the way you do.

The best articles will be published in the magazine.

The highs and lows of mountain weather

If you lived in the mountains like me, what would be your favourite type of weather? Glorious sunshine to sunbathe in? Deep snow to ski in?

Surprisingly, perhaps, it's the rain I most enjoy. Whether it's fine or heavy, spitting or pouring, I love wet weather! The rain on my face as I walk across the fields is cool and refreshing and always puts me in a good mood. It makes me feel optimistic about the future: after the rain, the sun comes out; after a shower the countryside is greener; and after my walk there's the promise of a warm fire and a cup of hot cocoa.

And what would you find it hard to put up with? Where I live it's the wind, which blows almost continuously for two weeks every August. Clothes are blown off washing lines, tiles are pulled off roofs and activities such as walking and cycling become very difficult. Who wouldn't feel bad-tempered by the end of it all?

But whatever the weather, I know I'd hate it if it was always the same.

2 The model answer is written in a fairly informal style. Find examples in the article of the following features.

Features	Examples
• A relevant title	*The highs and lows of mountain weather*
• Questions to involve the reader	_____
• A range of vocabulary related to the weather	_____
• Elements of informal language, e.g. contractions, phrasal verbs, linking words	_____
• Examples to illustrate a point	_____
• Adverbs expressing opinion or attitude	_____

3 Either: **a** Write your own answer to the question in exercise **1** on page 90,
or   **b** Write an answer to one of the following questions, in **140–190** words.

You see this announcement in an international magazine:

> **Competition**
>
> Write an article about a situation when you experienced severe weather conditions, telling our readers how you were affected by them.
>
> The best article will win a prize.

Write your **article**.

You see this notice in an international magazine:

> **People and places**
>
> We are looking for articles on the following question:
>
> *How does the climate in your country affect the way people feel and behave?*
>
> The best article will be published in our magazine.

Write your **article**.

Before you write

• Read more about writing articles on pages 134 and 135 of the Coursebook.
• Read the following advice about style and do exercise **4** below.
  In each of the questions above, the article will be written for readers of an international magazine. The style of your writing can be formal, neutral or informal, but it must be consistent throughout the article; in other words, you should not mix different styles in the same piece of writing.

---

4 The following extracts **a–c** were each written in answer to one of the three writing questions in exercises **1** and **3** above. Match each extract to one of the questions. Which of the extracts is not written in a consistent style?

a I've never really been keen on going out in the snow - and I can't understand why people get so excited about it. Your feet get soaking wet, your fingers nearly freeze off, and where's the fun in having a snowball pushed down the back of your neck? I'd love to have enough money to be able to get away from here when it snows.

b Moreover, the combination of harsh winters and warm summers has an interesting effect on the personality of those who live in the more remote, rural parts of my country. Inhabitants of these areas tend to withdraw into themselves between December and March, becoming shy and reserved. In spring, however, they undergo a transformation - it's really amazing! They're just so incredibly different - you'd almost think you were in another country!

c Huge waves crashed onto the beach, sending sand and stones high into the air. Gale-force winds caused destruction to buildings along the seafront, and made walking in the street extremely difficult. We spent the day sheltering in the lounge area of our hotel, wondering when, if ever, the storm would die down.

91

Reading and Use of English
Part 5

Multiple choice

1 You are going to read an article about an Italian cookery writer. For questions **1–6**, choose the answer (**A**, **B**, **C** or **D**) which you think fits best according to the text.

Anna Del Conte

Anna Del Conte is the woman who switched the British from tinned spaghetti to authentic Italian cooking.

The 87-year-old Italian cookery writer drives, cooks every day and has 'never, ever bought prepared, prefabricated food'. She is quick and decisive in her conclusions and gestures. Conversation ranges widely from the philosophical to

5 literature, to politics, to gossip about which chefs she rates and which she doesn't. The only concession she makes to her age is a nap in the afternoon. 'I work best after 5pm, and I read recently that many old people work best at that time,' she says.

10 Del Conte was born into a Milanese family who appreciated good food. Every day her mother would take her to shop for it in the grand emporia of the nearby via Montenapoleone, where the little girl would be given a wafer-thin slice of Parma ham by the shopkeepers. Her mother, though deeply

15 interested in food, was an intellectual who disdained the humdrum of everyday meal preparation. 'But she was a great cook. After the war, with no cook, she did it all. That's why Maria, our family cook, learnt so well.' Maria was with the family when Del Conte was a child. She loved little Anna, who

20 spent hours in the kitchen helping her.

Del Conte was lucky that, unlike an upper-class English girl of that era, for whom the kitchen would have been a forbidden place, and discussing food a social taboo, she gained an early appreciation of the traditional gastronomy of her own region,

25 Lombardy, as well as enjoying Maria's local dishes from Friuli. And her food education extended beyond choosing the right ingredients in shops: 'Though I was a city child, we would hunt for wild mushrooms in the woods, and pick dandelion and summer savory in the fields.'

30 Life in Milan after the war, when her family had lost everything, was far from joyful and, after a spell at university, Del Conte decided to come to England as an au pair. 'I ate well every day of my life until I came to England,' she says, for, though she was grateful for the kindness and skilful

35 cooking of her hostess in East Molesey, rationing in postwar Britain made it hard to produce anything approaching her diet in the Emilia-Romagna. 'The

40 food in Britain was terrible. Well, the meat was good, better than it is now, but the rest was terrible – how do you make a pudding when you can

45 only get salted butter?' she asks. Every Sunday she and her husband would go to church and then to the shops in Soho, among them Lina Stores and Camisa, which served the Italian community in London.

50 While bringing up her children, Del Conte worked part-time. It was in 1973, during a coaching session for Italian A-level, that she casually mentioned to her pupil that her brothers were constantly urging her to write a book of pasta recipes. That night the girl's father, a publisher, rang up and commissioned

55 Del Conte's first book, *Portrait of Pasta*, which appeared in 1976. It was a bold move, as in those days most people in Britain experienced pasta via macaroni cheese or tinned spaghetti. Her second book, the encyclopaedic *Gastronomy of Italy*, appeared in 1984. More books followed, each clearly

60 written, practical, and with recipes that taste authentically Italian but could be made easily by British cooks. They are full of recipes you want to cook every day.

Del Conte has a habit of deflecting praise by changing the subject. When I ask if she is proud of all that she has done

65 for food in Britain (for which she received the Lifetime Achievement Award of the British Guild of Food Writers in 2011) or promoting the understanding of Italian food in Britain (for which she received the Italian Order of Merit in 2010), she simply says, 'Well, it just happened. I was just there

70 at the right time. I couldn't do it now, because it has all been done. I was extremely lucky. My … excuse me …"cleverness" was in catching the right moment.'

1 In the first paragraph, the writer suggests that Del Conte
  A is too fussy about what she eats.
  B does not work many hours each day.
  C is very critical of others in her profession.
  D is not very typical of someone of her age.

2 The phrase 'disdained the humdrum' in lines 15–16 suggest that Del Conte's mother
  A believed cooking shared certain qualities with music.
  B felt that cooking was too dull an activity for her.
  C was too busy to devote much time to cooking.
  D enjoyed cooking but not all the time.

3 What do we learn about Del Conte's early relationship with food?

   A Her family background enabled her to eat only the best food.

   B Her favourite dishes were those based on local ingredients.

   C She was not allowed to talk about food as a child.

   D She had a very practical food education.

4 What explanation does Del Conte give for the poor quality of food in postwar Britain?

   A The dishes were all very similar.

   B There were not many good cooks in Britain.

   C It was difficult to obtain the right ingredients.

   D British people were unwilling to cook with foreign produce.

5 What does the writer say about Del Conte's first book?

   A Publishing it was a risk.

   B It was not an immediate success.

   C She wrote it with her family's help.

   D She initially had problems finding a publisher.

6 The impression we gain of Del Conte in the last paragraph is that she is

   A modest.

   B ambitious.

   C intelligent.

   D dissatisfied.

2 a Cover the reading text. Complete the extracts from the text **1–7** with one word. The words are the same for **a** and **b**.

   0 a While bringing __up__ her children, Del Conte worked part-time. (50)

   b That night the girl's father, a publisher, rang __up__ and commissioned Del Conte's first book ... (53–55)

   1 a Del Conte decided to come to England _____ an au pair. (32)

   b It was a bold move, _____ in those days most people in Britain experienced pasta via macaroni cheese or tinned spaghetti. (56–58)

   2 a It was in 1973, during a coaching session for Italian A-level, _____ she casually mentioned to her pupil that ... (50–52)

   b .... I ask if she is proud of all _____ she has done for food in Britain ... (64–65)

   3 a That's why Maria, our family cook, learnt so _____ . (17–18)

   b ... she gained an early appreciation of the traditional gastronomy of her own region, Lombardy, as _____ as enjoying Maria's local dishes from Friuli. (23–25)

   4 a Her mother, though deeply interested _____ food, was an intellectual ... (14–15)

   b 'My ... excuse me ... "cleverness" was _____ catching the right moment.' (71–72)

   5 a Conversation ranges widely from the philosophical ... to gossip about _____ chefs she rates and _____ she doesn't. (4–6)

   b ... promoting the understanding of Italian food in Britain (for _____ she received the Italian Order of Merit in 2010) ... (67–69)

   6 a The only concession she makes _____ her age is a nap in the afternoon. (6–7)

   b ... her brothers were constantly urging her _____ write a book of pasta recipes. (52–53)

   7 a ... unlike an upper-class English girl of that era, for whom the kitchen _____ have been a forbidden place ... (21–23)

   b Though I was a city child, we _____ hunt for wild mushrooms in the woods ... (27–28)

b Now uncover the reading text and check your answers. The line numbers are given in brackets.

Vocabulary

Wordlist on page 208 of the Coursebook

A Food and drink

1 Complete the sentences with the correct form of verbs from the box.

> bolt   chew   drink   eat   gulp   leave   sip   swallow

1 Come on, _____ up your dinner – don't _____ any food on your plate.
2 _____ helps break down the food you eat, making it easier to digest.
3 I don't have a glass for your juice – can you _____ it straight from the bottle?
4 My two-year-old nephew _____ a stone last night and had to go to hospital.
5 You're supposed to _____ hot tea, not _____ it down in two seconds!
6 She rushed in, _____ down her lunch and rushed straight out again.

2 Which word could be used to describe the food in each of the following cases? Match the adjectives in the box to a statement.

> ~~bitter~~ bland crunchy greasy rich savoury sickly sour spicy stodgy

0 This coffee really needs a little more sugar adding to it. ___*bitter*___
1 There's rather a lot of fat on these chips. _____
2 You've put a lot of butter and cream in this sauce. _____
3 No, it's not a sweet dish. It's got salt and a few herbs in it. _____
4 I'm sorry, I don't like this – it's like eating a lemon. _____
5 That chocolate mousse was far too sweet – it made me feel quite ill. _____
6 Sorry about the noise – this celery's just so fresh. _____
7 I'm not very keen on curry; it's too hot for me. _____
8 The food in our school canteen is very heavy; it takes ages to digest. _____
9 It hasn't really got a lot of flavour, has it? _____

B Health

Complete the sentences with a noun or adjective from the box.

Nouns:	ache attack bleed decay pressure
Adjectives:	black runny sore sprained stiff

1 I woke up with a _____ neck this morning. I need to get a new pillow.
2 Is it true that high blood _____ can lead to a heart _____ ?
3 If your nose is _____ , get a handkerchief and blow it.
4 The dentist says I've got dental caries – that's tooth _____ , or holes in the teeth.
5 I've got a very _____ throat – it really hurts when I swallow.
6 My ankle's not broken, just _____ : I twisted it coming down the stairs.
7 I ate too much, too quickly and now I've got a really bad stomach _____ .
8 A boy at school accidentally hit him in the face and gave him a _____ eye.
Then he walked into a door and gave himself a nose _____ !

C *Have*, *put*, *give* and *take*

Match **1–8** to **a–h** to make logical sentences.

1	He had both	**a**	plaster on her cut.
2	He had another	**b**	an injection in his leg.
3	They put him	**c**	own temperature.
4	She put a	**d**	operation on his leg.
5	They gave him	**e**	his legs in plaster for six weeks.
6	He gave her	**f**	pill for her headache.
7	She took a	**g**	on a course of antibiotics.
8	He took his	**h**	a prescription, which she took to the chemist's.

Language focus

 Grammar reference on pages 218–220 of the Coursebook

A Reported speech

The following comments from two teachers were recorded by Lynda Johnson when doing a survey at school on healthy living. Read the questions and comments and then complete the extracts from Lynda's report.

What do you do to keep fit?

Mr Bracewell: I enjoy all kinds of sport, particularly running – I'm competing in a marathon tomorrow.

Ms Hallam: I do aerobics every morning, but I'm thinking of taking up jogging instead.

Can you give us any advice about what to eat?

Mr Bracewell: Personally, I eat a lot of carbohydrates because of my running, but in general, a balanced diet is the best way to stay healthy.

Ms Hallam: The advice I always give to my students is that they shouldn't eat snacks between meals. And of course, everyone should eat a balanced diet.

Do you think diets are a good way to lose weight?

Mr Bracewell: I don't know – I've never needed to go on one!

Ms Hallam: I went on a diet once and I lost about five kilos. I wouldn't do it again, though – I like eating too much.

Healthy living

As part of a project on healthy living, I spoke last week to Mr Bracewell, the French teacher, and Ms Hallam, who teaches biology, and I asked them to comment on various aspects related to this topic.

Firstly, I asked both teachers what **(0)** _____*they did to keep fit*_____ . Mr Bracewell said he enjoyed all kinds of sports, particularly running: he added that
(1) _____ . Ms Hallam said **(2)** _____
every morning, but that **(3)** _____ instead.

When I asked them **(4)** _____ any advice about what to eat, both teachers recommended **(5)** _____ a balanced diet. Ms Hallam said that she always advised **(6)** _____ snacks between meals, and Mr Bracewell commented that he ate a lot of carbohydrates because of his running.

I then asked the teachers **(7)** _____ a good way to lose weight. Mr Bracewell replied that he did not know, because **(8)** _____ .
Ms Hallam said that **(9)** _____ and had lost five kilos. She went on to say that **(10)** _____ , however, as she
(11) _____ too much.

95

B Reporting verbs

Underline the correct alternative.

1 The waitress *suggested/recommended* me to try the oven-baked salmon.
2 Martin's personal trainer *encouraged/threatened* him to run a marathon.
3 A friend of mine has *offered/invited* me to stay at his house in Brighton.
4 Tara's teacher *warned/refused* her not to go outside without her coat on.
5 Joe's mum *explained/reminded* him to get off the bus at the train station.
6 For Luke's birthday, I *suggested/promised* going up in a hot-air balloon.
7 My tennis coach *persuaded/recommended* I wear a shirt made of cotton.
8 Who *told/said* you to end every line in this exercise with the letters 'on'?

C Countable and uncountable nouns

Cross out the alternative which cannot be used.

1 Have you heard *any/a/the* news about the accident?
2 I didn't speak *a large number/a great deal/a lot* of English when I was in London.
3 *Many/Several/Every* people in our neighbourhood have complained about the smell from the factory.
4 They didn't give us very much *advice/suggestion/information* about where to look for a cheap *guest house/hotel/accommodation* in the town.
5 Could you pass me a *piece/bar/slice* of bread, please?
6 **A:** Would you like *some/any/few* more chips?
   B: No, thanks. I've already got *plenty/much/enough*.
7 We haven't got *no/any/much* cheese left. Could you buy *a few/a little/some* on your way home tonight?
8 Come on, let's go out for a meal. We've still got *a little/little/plenty of* money.
9 I think I'll have *some more/another/any more* coffee.
10 Don't put *too much/another/any* more chicken in my sandwiches. A couple of slices is plenty.

Open cloze

Reading and Use of English Part 2

For questions **1–8**, read the text below and think of the word which best fits each gap. Use only **one** word in each gap. There is an example at the beginning **(0)**. Write your answers **IN CAPITAL LETTERS**.

Dining alone

The growing trend in UK restaurants **(0)** _NOT_ to accept reservations has a fortunate side-effect for the lone diner. A no-reservations policy can lead **(1)** _____ queues forming outside the more popular restaurants as diners wait **(2)** _____ a table to become available. Understandably, perhaps, some are far from happy about having to stand outside a doorway **(3)** _____ settling down to a relaxing meal. People in parties of four or more often have a long wait. **(4)** _____ , those who choose or are forced to dine alone usually have **(5)** _____ trouble at all getting a table and are seated almost immediately.

This is obviously good news for solo diners, **(6)** _____ now make up a significant percentage of the restaurant-going public in the UK. 'A table for one, please' is now a common request to waiters, and people sitting **(7)** _____ their own are no longer made to feel as if they are rather odd. They can hold up their head with confidence **(8)** _____ of trying to avoid unwelcome stares from fellow diners.

Word formation

For questions **1–8**, read the text below. Use the word given in capitals at the end of some of the lines to form a word that fits in the gap in the same line. There is an example at the beginning **(0)**. Write your answers **IN CAPITAL LETTERS**.

A knee operation

My brother took part in a skiing **(0)** _COMPETITION_ recently. He   **COMPETE**
didn't win any medals but he did receive a bad knee **(1)** _____ .   **INJURE**
He fell quite badly and for weeks afterwards he had **(2)** _____   **DIFFICULT**
walking properly. He eventually had to go into hospital for an operation,
from which he's currently recovering at home. He's been told to keep his
(3) _____ off the leg, so he spends his day on the sofa, reading   **WEIGH**
and watching films.
This temporary **(4)** _____ of mobility will be good for him; he's   **LOSE**
always rushing around, getting stressed out. **(5)** _____ , in most   **APPEAR**
cases, as long as there are no **(6)** _____ , people can resume   **COMPLICATE**
their normal activity within a few weeks of the operation. He says he's
already noticed an **(7)** _____ , and he's convinced he'll be back   **IMPROVE**
at work by the end of the month. To tell the **(8)** _____ , I think   **TRUE**
he should wait a little longer – he really could do with the break.

Transformations

For questions **1–6**, complete the second sentence so that it has a similar meaning to the first sentence, using the word given. **Do not change the word given.** You must use between **two** and **five** words, including the word given. Write your answers **IN CAPITAL LETTERS**.

1 I am not sure exactly how deep the harbour is.
   EXACT
   I am not sure _____ of the harbour.

2 We could not choose where we sat in the classroom.
   HAD
   We _____ we sat in the classroom.

3 Although the bus arrived late, we managed to get there on time.
   DESPITE
   We managed to get there on time, _____ of the bus.

4 She gave me very little help with the homework.
   NOT
   She did _____ help with the homework.

5 'Don't swim too far out,' she warned him.
   WARNED
   She _____ swim too far out.

6 'Did you buy a bandage, Tom?' asked Graham.
   HAD
   Graham asked Tom _____ a bandage.

Review, article and informal letter

A Planning

Match the writing questions **1–3** to the paragraph plans **A–C**.

1 You have seen this notice in your college's English-language magazine:

> ### Reviews needed
>
> We would like our readers to send us reviews of good or bad restaurants. Write about a restaurant you have been to recently. In your review, describe the restaurant and your meal, and say why you did or did not enjoy eating there.
>
> The best reviews will be published in the next edition.

Write your **review** in **140–190** words.

2 You have seen this announcement in an international magazine:

> ### The perfect meal
>
> *Write us an article describing your perfect meal.*
>
> *Where would you have it?*
>
> *Who would you be with?*
>
> *What would you eat?*
>
> *Don't forget to give reasons for your choices.*
>
> *The best articles will be published in next month's magazine.*

Write your **article** in **140–190** words.

3 Last weekend several of your relatives came to your home for a family meal to celebrate an important event. Write a letter to your English friend, telling him/her what you were celebrating and describing what you ate. You should also mention some things that happened during the celebrations.

Write your **letter** in **140–190** words.

A Title (e.g. Saying it with fish)
- Introduction (lively) saying where ('Blue Waves' seafood restaurant) and who with (parents)
- Give reason for the place (our favourite food, best seafood restaurant in town) and the people (way of saying thank you)
- Describe food and give reasons: crab (love it, never cook it at home), Bacalhau à Brás (cod – reminds me of holiday in Portugal)
- Closing comment – no better way to say thank you to parents for all they've done.

B
a Brief description of restaurant (name, location, type of food served) and say 'Worst meal I've ever had'

b Describe slow service, rude waiter, loud background music (and perhaps, no heating)

c Describe meal: tasteless soup, tough meat, cold vegetables

d Closing comments saying I would not recommend the restaurant to anyone

C
1 Opening: thank for birthday card. Mention 18th birthday meal
2 Briefly say who was there. Describe what ate – great!
3 One or two paragraphs on what happened:
   e.g. a Good things: surprise guest and/or present; sang songs/played games
         b Bad things: someone fell ill; family argument
4 Ending: ask about friend's 18th birthday

B Writing

1 When writing your answer you should aim to include various 'ingredients'. Match each writing type **1–3** to the appropriate list of 'ingredients' **a–c**.

1 Review   **2** Article   **3** Informal letter

a • interesting title to attract the reader's attention
- • direct statements and questions addressed to the reader
- • a lively, informal style to interest and engage the reader

b • appropriate opening and closing formulae
- • informal language and expressions
- • informal linking words, e.g. *and*, *but*, *so*

c • a clear statement of your opinion
- • a range of appropriate adjectives to show opinion
- • a recommendation

2 Write an answer to one of the questions in **Planning** on page 98 in **140–190** words. You may follow the relevant plan **(A–C)** or you may write your own. You should aim to include the relevant 'ingredients' from exercise **1** above.

For more information on each of the writing types you should look again at the Ready for Writing section in the Coursebook, as well as the following units:

	Coursebook	Workbook
Reviews	4, 9	7
Articles	2, 6, 10	3, 11
Informal letters and emails	1, 7	1, 10

3 Write an answer to one of the questions below. Choose a different writing type to the one you chose in exercise **2**. Don't forget to make a plan before you start to write.

Timing

In the exam you will have approximately 40 minutes to write each answer. Try following these guidelines when writing your answer to the question below:

5 minutes	Make a plan
30 minutes	Write your answer
5 minutes	Check your work

---

a You have seen this notice in your college English-language magazine:

> **Reviews needed**
>
> Do you regularly go to a gym or a sports centre? If so, could you write us a review? Include information on the equipment, facilities and customer service and say whether you would recommend the place to other people.
>
> The best reviews will be published in the next edition.

Write your **review** in **140–190** words.

b You have seen this announcement in an international magazine:

> **How to beat stress**
>
> Write an article giving us your tips for beating stress at work or in your studies.
>
> In particular, we'd like you to tell us:
> - how you prevent yourself from getting stressed.
> - how you relax and unwind if you're feeling stressed.
>
> The best articles will be published in next month's magazine.

Write your **article** in **140–190** words.

c You recently decided to lead a more healthy lifestyle. Write a letter to your pen friend describing the changes you have made and telling him/her what benefits you have noticed so far.

Write your **letter** in **140–190** words.

Reading and Use of English
Part 6

Gapped text

1 You are going to read an article in which a woman talks about her childhood. Six sentences have been removed from the article. Choose from the sentences **A–G** the one which fits each gap **(1–6)**. There is one extra sentence which you do not need to use.

Growing up in the countryside

Comedian Jo Brand recalls an idyllic childhood.

a badger

In 1962, when I was four, we moved from Clapham in south London to Kent. Back then it was all fields and apple orchards. For the first couple of years we lived on a modern estate, full of typical, boring three-bedroom houses with square lawns, a fence and a garden shed. But compared to Clapham it was
5 idyllic and we virtually skipped to school.

For us children, the excitement of moving to Kent was to do with being close to rabbits, foxes and different kinds of birds. We were always on the lookout for injured animals we could take care of. One day my father ran over a badger on his way home from work. **1**☐

Dad knew he shouldn't leave him in agony. For some reason he had a garden spade in his car boot. He took it out and tried
10 to kill the badger by hitting him on the head. **2**☐ My father had the city person's disease around animals, which means you can't bear to be cruel even when you're trying to be kind. A farmer came along, took the spade and with one blow put the badger out of his misery.

a hare

During the summer holidays after my first year at primary school, I was playing with my brothers, Matt and Bill, in the garden when we found an
15 injured hare. **3**☐ A cardboard box was found, and an appointment made at the vet, who said the hare had broken his leg. He put it in a splint and told us what to feed him and how to care for him.

By this time, the three of us had named the hare Harold. He was put into a rabbit hutch in the garden and we fought over whose turn it was to feed
20 him dandelion leaves. After a couple of weeks we were allowed to take the splint off and he started to hop about the garden. I thought he'd stay with us and be our pet. **4**☐

The three of us started shrieking and I started crying. Although it happened quickly, in my memory, it's like that bit in slow motion from the film *Chariots of Fire*, when they're all training on the beach. **5**☐ She caught Harold in mid-air with one
25 hand on each leg, and landed in next-door's garden.

He stayed for another week or so. **6**☐ Midway through my first week back at school, I came home and he was gone. It was a huge tragedy.

A But he didn't have the heart to do it.

B There's even music playing in my head as I picture my mother starting to run, then hurdling over the fence.

C So we called out to Mum, who was busy in the kitchen, and asked her to help.

D My mother took pity on him, placed him in a box and took him straight to the vet.

E He got out of the car and saw he was badly hurt but still alive.

F Then our parents told us that wild animals don't want to stay cooped up in a hutch like a pet.

G But one evening, while we were playing with him, he made a bid for freedom and dashed off towards the fence.

2 a Cover the reading text. Complete the extracts from the text **1–8** with a preposition from the box.

for (x2)   of   on (x2)   out of   over   through   with

1 The excitement of moving to Kent was **to do** _____ being close to rabbits, foxes and different kinds of birds. (6–7)

2 We were always _____ **the lookout for** injured animals we could **take care** _____ . (7)

3 One day my father **ran** _____ a badger on his way home from work. (7–8)

4 A farmer came along, took the spade and with one blow **put** the badger _____ **his misery**. (11–12)

5 He put it in a splint and told us what to feed him and how to **care** _____ him. (16–17)

6 **Midway** _____ my first week back at school, I came home and he was gone. (26)

7 My mother **took pity** _____ him, placed him in a box and took him straight to the vet. (D)

8 But one evening … he **made a bid** _____ **freedom** and dashed off towards the fence. (G)

b Now uncover the text and check your answers. The line numbers are given in brackets.

3 Match the meanings **a–h** to the expressions in bold in exercise **2a**.
a felt sorry for ____took pity on____
b kill an animal that is suffering _____
c related to _____
d in the middle of _____
e tried to escape _____
f hit with a vehicle _____
g watching carefully in order to find _____
h look after _____ and _____

Vocabulary

Wordlist on page 208 of the Coursebook

A The arts

Across

1 a person who creates objects out of materials such as wood, stone or metal

4 you go to the theatre to see one

6 Romeo dies in the third _____ of Act V of Shakespeare's play *Romeo and Juliet*.

7 operas are performed in an opera _____

8 a painting showing a view of the countryside

10 you go to an art gallery to see an _____ of paintings

Down

1 the area in a theatre on which the actors perform

2 adjective to describe a painting or other object which is extremely valuable

3 a large group of musicians who play many different instruments together

4 a painting of a person

5 a person who writes music, especially classical music

7 a concert _____ is a place where concerts are given

9 collective noun for actors in 4 across

B Paraphrasing

Complete the second sentence in each pair with a word from the box. The sentence pairs have the same meaning.

| attention | branch | criticism | doubt | face | fetch | question | sensation |

1 Punk gave music a new feel.   Punk changed the _____ of music.
2 I am very sure about that.   I am in no _____ about that.
3 The theft causes us to consider security.   The theft raises the _____ of security.
4 Some have disapproved of the film.   The film has come in for some _____ .
5 The play created a lot of excitement.   The play caused a great _____ .
6 People talked a lot about the book.   The book became the focus of _____ .
7 I want to write different types of things.   I want to _____ out in my writing.
8 How much was the artwork sold for?   How much did the artwork _____ ?

C Parts of animals

Complete the sentences with nouns from the box.

| beak | claws | feather | fin | fur | gills | hooves | mane | paw | whiskers |

1 Amy was the first to spot the shark; she saw its _____ sticking out of the water.
2 This bird uses its thick, heavy _____ to crack open and eat large seeds and nuts.
3 With his bushy beard and thick _____ of brown hair, he reminded me of a lion.
4 My new digital camera is small, very thin and as light as a _____ .
5 They created the sound of horses' _____ by hitting two coconut halves together.
6 I hate it when the cat comes and sits on my lap, then suddenly digs its sharp _____ into my leg.
7 If you hold your hand out in front of the dog, he'll give you his _____ , as if he's shaking hands with you.
8 I'm strongly opposed to the killing of animals to make _____ coats.
9 I read that cats usually have 24 _____ , 12 on each side of their face.
10 Most aquatic animals use _____ to breathe underwater.

D Verbs followed by prepositions

Complete the sentences with the correct prepositions.

1 I'd like to congratulate Ruth ____ gaining promotion and thank her ____ all her hard work in this department.
2 You criticize me ____ what I wear and prevent me ____ doing what I want. It's not fair!
3 Instead of apologizing ____ crashing into the back of my car, he accused me ____ driving carelessly and blamed me ____ causing the accident.
4 I've already told you off twice ____ making a lot of noise. I can't concentrate ____ what I'm doing.
5 Please forgive me ____ breaking your vase. I insist ____ buying a replacement.

Language focus

 Grammar reference on pages 220–221 of the Coursebook

A Hypothetical situations

1 Complete the sentences with the correct form of the verb in brackets.

1 I wish I _____ (have) a car. I'm fed up with having to walk everywhere.

2 I wish you _____ (not/make) so much noise. I'm trying to concentrate.

3 The sea looks wonderful. If only I _____ (bring) my swimming costume.

4 The printer's not working. I wish I _____ (know) how to fix it.

5 I wish it _____ (stop) raining. I want to go to the shops.

6 I'd rather you _____ (not/tell) anyone about it yet.

7 My wife wants to go to Italy on holiday, but I'd rather _____ (go) to Spain.

8 It's time I _____ (buy) some new shoes. These ones have got holes in them.

2 What would you say in each of the following situations? Complete the sentences.

0 Your exams are in two weeks' time and you haven't done any revision yet.
  It's high time I _____ *started revising for my exams* _____ .

1 Your classmate hasn't got a watch and is always asking you what time it is.
  It's about time you _____ .

2 Your friend said he'd phone you at 8.30, but there's a film on TV which starts at 8.15.
  I'd rather you _____ .

3 You're trying to tell your brother something but he keeps interrupting.
  I wish you _____ .

4 You have an exam on Saturday so you won't be able to watch the cup final.
  I wish _____ .

5 Someone stole your video camera on holiday. It wasn't insured.
  If only _____ .

B Prepositions and gerunds

Complete the second sentence so that it has a similar meaning to the first sentence, using the word in brackets. **Do not change the word in brackets.** Write **four** words in each gap, including the word in brackets.

0 Paul teaches English and he also does some translation work. **(addition)**
  Paul does some translation work *in addition to teaching* English.

1 Don't pay for it all now; you can make monthly payments. **(instead)**
  You can make monthly payments _____ it all now.

2 Naomi felt ill but we still played tennis. **(despite)**
  We played tennis _____ well.

3 Even though Mike's unemployed, he can still afford to go on holiday. **(spite)**
  Mike can still afford to go on holiday, _____ unemployed.

4 We missed the start of the film because Josh arrived at the cinema late. **(result)**
  We missed the start of the film as a _____ to the cinema late.

5 She brought up three children on her own and looked after her sick father, too. **(well)**
  She brought up three children on her own, _____ care of her sick father.

Multiple-choice cloze

For questions **1–8**, read the text below and decide which answer (**A**, **B**, **C** or **D**) best fits each gap. There is an example at the beginning (**0**).

Raining animals

There are (**0**) ____ examples of strange occurrences in the animal world, and none more bizarre than those which (**1**) ____ animals falling from the sky. Showers of fish have been reported on various (**2**) ____ throughout history, including as recently as 2010 in the remote Australian town of Lajamanu. Hundreds of small white fish, many of them still alive, were seen falling from rainclouds over the (**3**) ____ of two days. It is believed the fish were (**4**) ____ up by a small whirlwind during a thunderstorm and then (**5**) ____ on the confused residents of the small desert town, which is over 300 miles from the nearest river.

A similar explanation was (**6**) ____ for the downpour of frogs in Rákóczifalva, Hungary, in June 2010; and the shower of worms in Jennings, Louisiana, in July 2007. (**7**) ____ , experts remain uncertain of the causes of the clouds of dead tadpoles which fell on the Japanese region of Ishikawa throughout June 2009, as there had been no reports of (**8**) ____ winds around that time.

0	**A** plenty	**B** wide	**C** <u>numerous</u>	**D** full
1	**A** consist	**B** compose	**C** involve	**D** interest
2	**A** events	**B** occasions	**C** times	**D** incidents
3	**A** course	**B** way	**C** gap	**D** path
4	**A** sipped	**B** risen	**C** bolted	**D** sucked
5	**A** fallen	**B** loaded	**C** dumped	**D** tripped
6	**A** brought	**B** done	**C** given	**D** put
7	**A** Furthermore	**B** However	**C** Equally	**D** Additionally
8	**A** hard	**B** tall	**C** thick	**D** strong

Open cloze

For questions **1–8**, read the text below and think of the word which best fits each gap. Use only **one** word in each gap. There is an example at the beginning (**0**). Write your answers **IN CAPITAL LETTERS**.

Animal mummies

Over the centuries millions of animal mummies (**0**) <u>*HAVE*</u> been discovered in Egypt, either lying alongside human mummies, or in their own separate cemeteries. But why were they put there?

Some, it seems, were pets; in the same way that possessions were buried (**1**) _____ the use of the dead in the afterlife, a favourite cat, dog or monkey would (**2**) _____ sacrificed in order to keep the deceased company there. Other animals, however, were intended (**3**) _____ gifts to the gods; a crocodile to please Sobek or a cow for Hathor. Whole catacombs were dedicated to particular animals, such as cats, dogs or birds, (**4**) _____ were buried in large numbers, possibly to mark a religious festival. (**5**) _____ animal was considered too small or insignificant for mummification: snakes, beetles, fish of all sizes and even the eggs of birds and reptiles.

(**6**) _____ animal mummies were clearly very important to the ancient Egyptians, few studies have been carried out on the subject, perhaps because (**7**) _____ has always been more interest (**8**) _____ human mummies.

Reading and Use of English
Part 3

Word formation

For questions **1–8**, read the text below. Use the word given in capitals at the end of some of the lines to form a word that fits in the gap in the same line. There is an example at the beginning **(0)**. Write your answers **IN CAPITAL LETTERS**.

North-Eastern Art

The North-East of England has developed something of a reputation

for unusual works of public art, and large metallic **(0)** _SCULPTURES_   **SCULPT**

are now fairly commonplace in the region. The best known of these is

the 200-ton steel figure, *Angel of the North*, erected in Gateshead at the

(1) _____ cost of £800,000. Many local people were   **CONSIDER**

horrified at the **(2)** _____ to spend such a large sum of   **DECIDE**

money on a 65-foot metal structure. Nevertheless, the Angel is

(3) _____ one of the most frequently viewed artworks in the   **POSSIBLE**

world, seen **(4)** _____ by over 90,000 passing motorists. A   **DAY**

number of **(5)** _____ in Hartlepool were similarly upset when   **RESIDE**

they were greeted one day by the **(6)** _____ of 15 giant,   **SEE**

metal balls on a traffic roundabout in the town centre. They described

the payment of £70,000 for the spheres as **(7)** _____ and felt   **RESPONSIBLE**

the money should have been spent on something which would be more

directly **(8)** _____ to the local population.   **BENEFIT**

Reading and Use of English
Part 4

Transformations

For questions **1–6**, complete the second sentence so that it has a similar meaning to the first sentence, using the word given. **Do not change the word given.** You must use between **two** and **five** words, including the word given. Write your answers **IN CAPITAL LETTERS**.

1 The president offered his congratulations to the players when they won the cup.
   CONGRATULATED
   The president _____ the cup.

2 'I'm sorry I'm late,' said Adrian to Chrissie.
   APOLOGIZED
   Adrian _____ late.

3 'Elena, you've left mud on the carpet!' said her father.
   ACCUSED
   Elena's father _____ mud on the carpet.

4 It is not new for teachers to be criticized by parents.
   ABOUT
   There is nothing _____ in for criticism
   from parents.

5 I'm sorry I didn't continue with my piano lessons.
   NOT
   I wish _____ up my piano lessons.

6 I should have listened to my parents' advice.
   ATTENTION
   If only _____ my parents' advice.

Writing
Parts 1 and 2

Read the Writing questions below. Before you write any answers, do the preparation exercises on page 107.

Part 1

You **must** answer this question. Write your answer in **140–190** words in an appropriate style.

1 In your English class you have been talking about the relevance of museums to young people. Now, your English teacher has asked you to write an essay.

Write an essay using all the notes and give reasons for your point of view.

Write your **essay**.

> Essay question
> There is not enough to interest young people in museums. Do you agree?
>
> Notes
> Write about:
> 1 types of exhibits
> 2 what interests young people
> 3 .... (your own idea)

Part 2

Write an answer to one of the questions **2–4** in this part. Write your answer in **140–190** words in an appropriate style.

2 You are studying in England and you see the following advertisement in a local newspaper:

> **TEMPORARY WORK IN A PET SHOP**
>
> We require a part-time shop assistant for three months. Duties include: feeding and caring for pets, serving in shop, advising customers on animal care.
> • love and knowledge of animals essential
> • previous experience of shop work preferred
> Foreign students welcome: must have reasonable level of spoken English
> Contact: Mr P. Sayers.

Write your **letter of application** to Mr Sayers.

3 The school where you learn English has decided to organize a day trip to a place of cultural or historical interest. You have been asked to write a report for the principal suggesting places to visit. In your report you should explain what students would learn from and enjoy about going to these places.

Write your **report**.

4 You see the following advertisement in a magazine for pet lovers.

> **Writing Competition**
> We would like to receive your articles with the following title:
> MY SPECIAL FRIEND
> Write to us about your pet, telling our readers how it came to be in your family and what makes it so special.
> The writer of the best entry will receive a year's supply of food for their pet.

Write your **article**.

A Ideas for Part 1

The following comments were made in answer to the three points in the Notes for question **1**. Tick ✓ those comments which agree with the statement in the essay question and put a cross ✗ next to those which disagree. The first one has been done for you.

1

a Increasingly, museums offer exhibits which are interactive and fun. ✗

b There are too many uninteresting objects in glass cases.

c Pushing buttons to make lights flash does not always capture a child's imagination.

2

a Teenagers would rather play video games than visit a museum.

b Being young does not mean you cannot appreciate great works of art.

c Young people are not interested in spending a morning looking at paintings.

3

a Many museums provide workshops specifically designed for children.

b Art museums should do more to bring paintings to life.

c Some museums put on plays representing important moments in history.

B Language preparation

1 Complete the sentences **1–10** with the correct phrases from the box.

a great deal about	a large number of	aim of this report	have no experience of
I like most about her	express an interest	my opinion	option would be to
	people believe that	that struck me	

   1 The _____ is to offer suggestions for …

   2 In _____ , museums could do more to capture young people's interest.

   3 Although I _____ working in a pet shop, I spent the last two summers helping my uncle in his newsagent's.

   4 The first thing _____ about her was her lovely smooth fur.

   5 Some _____ young people find museums boring.

   6 Students would learn _____ life in the Middle Ages on the trip.

   7 What _____ is her lively nature and almost limitless energy.

   8 I am writing to _____ in the job I saw advertised in the *York Gazette*.

   9 One _____ visit the Roman Palace near Chichester.

  10 However, _____ museums do offer engaging activities for children.

2 In answer to which question **(1–4)** is each sentence written?
Sentence 1, Question 3

Writing task

Write an answer to the Part 1 question. Then choose one of the Part 2 questions and write an answer.

For more information on each of the writing types you should look again at the Ready for Writing section in the Coursebook, as well as the following units:

Task type	Coursebook	Workbook
Essay	3, 5, 8	4, 6, 9
Letter of application	2	5
Report	4, 12	8
Article	2, 6, 10	3, 11

Multiple choice

1 You are going to read a newspaper article about body language. For questions **1–6**, choose the answer (**A**, **B**, **C** or **D**) which you think fits best according to the text.

The truth behind body language

Non-verbal actions can send different – and more genuine – messages than words, discovers **Karen Hainsworth**

Words convey the messages that we want others to hear, but our bodies may tell a different story. Whether we express our problems
5 to our colleagues with a hunched back and sad, downcast eyes, or our enthusiasm for life with a cheerful spring in our step, our bodies are constantly sending out messages. And understanding these clues that we unavoidably offer each other is an essential part of effective communication.

10 'People vary enormously in their ability to detect non-verbal cues,' says Dr Peter Bull, psychologist at the University of York. 'Those who tend to be good at detecting emotions and getting the timing right when raising tricky subjects are usually picking up others' moods through these non-verbal clues,' he says. 'But it's important to be emotionally intelligent when dealing with the real messages that are coming through. There's little point in being a skilled decoder of subtle signals if your colleagues' more
15 genuine emotions overwhelm you with anxiety, anger or irritation.'

The ability to manipulate your own body language is suggested as an essential skill when it comes to making a good impression. 'If you're aiming to communicate interest and enthusiasm at an interview, for example, confident body language can help to convey a message that is consistent,' says Bull. 'General facial cues suggesting alertness, while showing that you are listening, can help. And your tone
20 of voice should be lively and interested.'

Though we can portray a false emotion to a certain extent, few can fool a skilled observer, who is likely to detect the micro-expressions that we constantly make. We may smile when we are miserable, but a body language expert will know we're faking it. Genuine smiles use the tiny muscles around the eyes, but a false smile involves only the mouth.

25 It's not that difficult to modify grosser signals, however. And we can make a good start by developing a level of self-awareness. 'It's important to listen to what our own bodies are doing,' says Dr Betty Rudd, the chartered counselling psychologist. If you want to give the impression of confidence at work, first recognize how much space you are taking up. 'Think about letting go of the tension in your muscles; allow the floor or the chair to take their weight,' says Rudd. 'Think of your back spreading out and
30 widening and lengthening.' And she suggests maintaining eye contact with the person you are dealing with, rather than constantly averting your gaze. 'These little things can make a huge impact and you will feel more grounded and secure,' she says.

Once you become aware of these subtle signs, you increase your power to communicate effectively. When your body is saying the same thing as your words, it shows consistency or congruence and that
35 has enormous impact. But people will often use incongruence to get less comfortable information across. 'They may say something that makes them sound quite interested in you, but their body language suggests they are not,' says Bull. 'They may feel they cannot come out and say, "I'm not interested", so what they do is say it through a lukewarm, uninterested non-verbal style.'

Decoding the real message can be a tricky business and becomes even more complicated when different
40 cultures begin to mix. But whether that's the culture of a country or company, you can avoid putting your foot in it by watching others closely and observing the subtleties of non-verbal cues, while noting the unspoken messages that accompany the words.

1 In the first paragraph we are told that
   A it is inadvisable to express our true feelings through our posture.
   B the words we speak are inconsistent with the gestures we make.
   C a correct interpretation body language is important for communication.
   D our body is the only true indicator of meaning.

2 Dr Bull says that an understanding of body language needs to be accompanied by
   A a suitable emotional response.
   B an ability to talk about difficult topics.
   C a tendency to express one's emotions.
   D an appropriately high level of intelligence.

3 In an interview situation, Dr Bull says it is important to
   A be more attentive than usual.
   B ensure your whole face is visible.
   C speak in a high-pitched voice.
   D use appropriate body language.

4 What is meant by 'we're faking it' in line 23?
   A we are incapable of laughing
   B we are making fun of others
   C we are trying to cheer ourselves up
   D we are pretending to be happier than we really are

5 What does Dr Rudd say to people who want to appear confident?
   A Spread out your whole body to occupy a large space.
   B Adopt a casual posture when standing or sitting.
   C Avoid looking away from people you are talking to.
   D Imagine you are sitting or lying down.

6 According to Dr Bull, some people use body language
   A to express what they dare not say openly.
   B to show how uncomfortable they feel.
   C to hide their true feelings for someone.
   D to conform to the rules of their culture.

2 Complete column **A** below by writing the noun form of the words for **1–8**. All the nouns appear in the reading text. Then complete comumn **B** by writing the noun form of the words for **9–16**. Use the same suffixes as in column **A**.

A

enthusiastic		*enthusiasm*
anxious	1	
angry	2	
irritate	3	
able	4	
alert	5	
confident	6	
weigh	7	
subtle	8	

B

optimistic		*optimism*
weak	9	
various	10	
credible	11	
certain	12	
persistent	13	
complicate	14	
complain	15	
hungry	16	

Vocabulary

Phrasal verb list on pages 130–132; Lexical phrase list on pages 133–134

A Phrasal verbs with *turn*

Complete the sentences with particles from the box.

down	into	off	on	out	up

1 They offered her the job but she turned it _____ because the salary was so low.
2 I was furious! We arranged to meet at 6 o'clock, but he didn't turn _____ until 7.
3 This building was a dance hall before they turned it _____ a cinema.
4 As soon as he gets up, he turns _____ the television and spends the next three hours watching the cartoons.
5 We got talking, and it turned _____ that we both went to the same school.
6 We've gone too far. We should have turned _____ this road at the last set of traffic lights.

109

B Expressions with *turn*

Match **1–8** to **a–h**.

1 My great-grandfather lived to 106.
2 My mum's feeling a little depressed.
3 She looked extremely cold.
4 Let's check the homework.
5 She knew we'd been up to no good.
6 I did the washing up yesterday.
7 She helped me so I'll help her.
8 She rushed to the hospital to be with him.

a Her face and hands had turned blue.
b Turn to page 42, everyone.
c He was born at the turn of the last century.
d One good turn deserves another.
e She's just turned 40.
f His condition had taken a turn for the worse.
g It's your turn to do it today.
h She turned a blind eye to it, though.

C Revision

Complete the sentences with the correct form of verbs from the box. Use each verb twice.

do	get	give	make	put	take

0 He cut himself quite badly, so he was __*taken*__ to hospital, where he was __*given*__ an anti-tetanus injection.

1 Recently we've been having problems _____ our son to _____ his homework.

2 I had considered _____ research, until I found out just how much time and effort I would need to _____ into it.

3 A lot of these off-piste skiers are selfish; as well as _____ their own lives at risk, they endanger those of the rescue services who are called out to help them when they _____ into trouble.

4 Check your work after you've finished to _____ sure you haven't _____ any silly mistakes.

5 His exam marks are always good but he usually _____ the impression in class that he isn't _____ any notice at all of what I'm saying.

D Expressions with *make* and *do*

Match **1–7** to **a–g**. Complete the sentences with the correct form of *make* or *do*.

Example: 1 e

1 He could __*do*__ so much better. He just needs
2 He _____ nothing but watch television. He could
3 His bedroom could _____ with a clean. He has
4 He should _____ some physical exercise. It'll
5 He'll need to _____ up his mind soon what
6 I missed the speech he _____ but I know it had
7 I'm not sure what job he _____ now but I know

a he _____ a good living from it.
b course he wants to_____ .
c something to _____ with art.
d help me _____ the housework.
e to __*make*__ more effort.
f _____ such a mess in it.
g _____ him good.

Language focus

Grammar reference on page 221 of the Coursebook

A Compound adjectives

Write phrases containing compound adjectives to describe **1–9**.

0 a doctor who received his training in Britain   *a British-trained doctor*

1 a car which they make in Spain   _____

2 a guide who speaks Russian   _____

3 a company which has its base in London   _____

4 a supermarket chain whose owners are French   _____

5 a cruise lasting ten days   _____

6 a woman who is 29   _____

7 a book with 650 pages   _____

8 a film lasting four hours   _____

9 a conference from 26th to 28th March inclusive   _____

B Expressing purpose

1 The following sentences tell a story about Ana. Match the actions **1–9** to the reasons **a–i**.
Example: 1 c

Action	Reason
1 Ana went to Dublin last month.	**a** She thought it might be cold there.
2 She went on her own, without her Spanish friends.	**b** She didn't want her parents to worry about her.
3 She took a lot of warm clothes.	**c** She wanted to study English.
4 Her host family had learnt a few words of Spanish.	**d** She might go back to Ireland next year.
5 Ana hired a car in Dublin.	**e** She didn't want to speak any Spanish.
6 She bought some guidebooks.	**f** She might not have understood any English.
7 She phoned home a few times.	**g** She doesn't want to forget what she learnt.
8 She's just signed up for an English course in Madrid.	**h** She wanted to see the rest of the country.
9 She has kept her guidebooks.	**i** She wanted to be able to read about the different places before visiting them.

2 Join each pair of sentences from exercise **1** using expressions of purpose from the box. Make any other necessary changes.

in case   in order   (not) to   so as   so that

1   *Ana went to Dublin last month in order to study English.*

2 _____

3 _____

4 _____

5 _____

6 _____

7 _____

8 _____

9 _____

C Ability

In five of the sentences there is a mistake in the part which is underlined. Find the mistakes and rewrite the sentences so that they are correct.

1 I could dance like that when I was your age.

_____

2 Trevor could mend the washing machine yesterday; it's working perfectly now.

_____

3 I couldn't do the homework last night – it was far too difficult.

_____

4 He could hear someone moving about in the kitchen. He went downstairs to investigate.

_____

5 I offered to help him but he said he could do it on his own.

_____

6 I've never could swim very well.

_____

7 I don't understand why he's the manager; he's incapable to organize anything.

_____

8 Did you manage to get in touch with Stephen last night?

_____

9 Jane's very busy, so she won't can come until later.

_____

10 They didn't succeed to get into the final last year; they were beaten 3–1 in the semi-finals.

_____

Reading and Use of English
Part 2

Open cloze

For questions **1–8**, read the text below and think of the word which best fits each gap. Use only **one** word in each gap. There is an example at the beginning **(0)**. Write your answers **IN CAPITAL LETTERS**.

A terrifying ordeal

Kevin Nicolle was **(0)** _ON_ his way home after visiting friends when disaster struck, and his quiet Sunday afternoon drive **(1)** _____ into a terrifying 135mph ordeal. The accelerator on his car jammed and the brakes failed. For almost 60 miles, Nicolle, 25, desperately tried to avoid crashing **(2)** _____ lorries and other cars.

As he passed the town of Thirsk, he took his foot off the accelerator, but the car speeded up **(3)** _____ of slowing down. 'The pedal was stuck to the floor. I was terrified, hysterical and crying,' he said. Nicolle called the police, **(4)** _____ sent four patrol cars and a helicopter. For a while he was able to bring his speed down to 70mph **(5)** _____ using the brakes, but they soon burnt out. 'I couldn't turn the ignition off because it would have disabled the power steering and made it even **(6)** _____ dangerous,' he said. As he drove, he sounded his horn and flashed his lights **(7)** _____ warn other vehicles.

(8) _____ the end, Nicolle crashed and turned his car over when attempting to avoid a queue of cars at a roundabout. He left the car with hardly a scratch.

Reading and Use of English *Part 1*

Multiple-choice cloze

For questions **1–8**, read the text below and decide which answer (**A**, **B**, **C** or **D**) best fits each gap. There is an example at the beginning (**0**).

Basic English

In the 1920s, psychologist Charles Kay Ogden developed what he termed Basic English, also (**0**) ____ as Simple English. It (**1**) ____ of 850 core words for expressing everyday meanings, (**2**) ____ supplementary lists of over a thousand specialist words related to such areas as science, commerce, literature and religion. Ogden (**3**) ____ verbs to be an obstacle to meaning and felt the elimination of verbs and their conjugations would be a very (**4**) ____ simplification, so he included just 18 of them in his core list.

The simplified language was (**5**) ____ as an aid for teaching English as a Second Language. It achieved its (**6**) ____ popularity shortly after the Second World War and received the support of Winston Churchill, who saw it as a tool for world peace. However, it has had many critics, the main complaint being that it is too restricted and (**7**) ____ range and expressiveness. The choice of words is also felt to be too (**8**) ____ influenced by Ogden's personal world-view, and there is no actual proof that it makes learning English simpler.

0	**A** called	**B** entitled	**C** regarded	**D** <u>known</u>
1	**A** contains	**B** consists	**C** concerns	**D** composes
2	**A** as well	**B** in addition	**C** along with	**D** more than
3	**A** pretended	**B** suggested	**C** seemed	**D** considered
4	**A** welcome	**B** grateful	**C** thankful	**D** appreciative
5	**A** aimed	**B** intended	**C** thought	**D** looked
6	**A** longest	**B** grandest	**C** largest	**D** greatest
7	**A** fails	**B** lacks	**C** extracts	**D** deletes
8	**A** heavily	**B** hardly	**C** roughly	**D** mostly

Reading and Use of English *Part 3*

Word formation

For questions **1–8**, read the text below. Use the word given in capitals at the end of some of the lines to form a word that fits in the gap in the same line. There is an example at the beginning (**0**). Write your answers **IN CAPITAL LETTERS**.

Saving languages

Linguist Jan Frupps makes his living by saving (**0**) *ENDANGERED*	**DANGER**
languages. The professor regularly goes to some of the most remote and	
(**1**) _____ places on earth to research such languages and	**ACCESS**
make detailed (**2**) _____ records. The work can be difficult,	**WRITE**
as some tribes are deeply (**3**) _____ of outsiders and think	**SUSPICION**
that people like Professor Frupp, with their (**4**) _____	**END**
curiosity and foreign ways, have come to steal their language and culture.	
Research trips can sometimes be very (**5**) _____ and some	**EVENT**
linguists have been imprisoned or threatened with guns while working in	
countries where the (**6**) _____ situation is unstable. According	**POLITICS**
to Frupp, the (**7**) _____ of a language begins when the younger	**APPEAR**
generation no longer uses it. 'If we can document a language before it	
becomes extinct, we can help to preserve the (**8**) _____ which	**KNOW**
is possessed by the people who speak it,' he explains.	

Reading and Use of English
Part 4

Transformations

For questions **1–6**, complete the second sentence so that it has a similar meaning to the first sentence, using the word given. **Do not change the word given.** You must use between **two** and **five** words, including the word given. Write your answers **IN CAPITAL LETTERS**.

1 The two sides were unable to reach an agreement.

   SUCCEED

   The two sides _____ an agreement.

2 He may be 50, but he can run a marathon in under three hours.

   CAPABLE

   He may be 50, but he _____ a marathon in under three hours.

3 He wore an extra pair of socks to avoid getting cold feet.

   SO

   He wore an extra pair of socks _____ get cold feet.

4 Jake isn't trying to improve his handwriting.

   EFFORT

   Jake is _____ improve his handwriting.

5 Lucy might arrive later so let's save a piece of cake for her.

   CASE

   Let's save a piece of cake for Lucy _____ up later.

6 They tried twice to find the missing climber but without success.

   MADE

   They _____ attempts to find the missing climber.

Writing
Parts 1 and 2

Do the following Writing paper in 80 minutes.

Part 1

You **must** answer this question. Write your answer in **140–190** words in an appropriate style.

1 In your English class you have been talking about English as a global language. Now, your English teacher has asked you to write an essay.

   Write an essay using all the notes and give reasons for your point of view.

   Essay question

   It is better to learn English first, before learning other foreign languages. Do you agree?

   Notes

   Write about:
   1 reasons for learning a language
   2 how easy or difficult the language is
   3 .... (your own idea)

   Write your **essay**.

Part 2

Write an answer to **one** of the questions **2–4** in this part. Write your answer in **140–190** words in an appropriate style.

How to go about it
Select your Part 2 task carefully. Consider, in particular, whether you will be able to demonstrate a good range of vocabulary and structures when answering the task.   Plan your answer carefully. Follow the checklist of points for planning and checking your work on page 193 of the Coursebook.

2 Your school's English-language magazine is asking students to give opinions on the coursebooks they have been using. Write a review of *Ready for First*, giving your views on the content and design of the book. You should say how well you think it prepares students for the exam and how much it has helped you improve your English.

Write your **review**.

3 This is part of an email you have received from your American friend, James.

I'm making good progress learning your language and I'm in the advanced class now. My teacher says I should watch original version films – can you recommend two or three in your language that might be suitable? It doesn't matter if they're not very good – it's the language that's important.

Thanks

James

Write your **email**.

4 You have seen this announcement in an international magazine:

What is success?

What do you understand by 'success'?

What is the best way to achieve it?

The best articles will be published in next month's magazine.

Write your **article**.

Listening bank

1 Lifestyle

Listening
Part 3 **Multiple matching** **1.1–1.5**

1 You will hear five short extracts in which people are talking about moving to another country. Before you do the exam task in exercise **2**, listen and match the people in the box to the five speakers.

college student	doctor	manager	school pupil	teacher

Speaker 1 _____   Speaker 4 _____

Speaker 2 _____   Speaker 5 _____

Speaker 3 _____

2 Listen to the five speakers and choose from the list **A–H** what each speaker says. Use the letters only once. There are three extra letters which you do not need to use.

A I was very disappointed by the whole experience.

B I was interested in discovering new things.

C I was surprised by the number of English people there.

D I thought the cost of living was OK.

E I found it hard to adapt to the change of routine.

F Communication was sometimes difficult.

G I was concerned about losing my old friends.

H I missed my family a lot.

Speaker 1 [| 1]
Speaker 2 [| 2]
Speaker 3 [| 3]
Speaker 4 [| 4]
Speaker 5 [| 5]

3a Complete the extracts from the listening with the correct form of verbs from the box. The verb you require in each pair of extracts (**a** and **b**) is the same.

~~get~~	look	make	set	turn

0 a … my dad ___got___ transferred.

  b … there's a lot to ___get___ your head round.

1 a I had to _____ the alarm for seven o'clock.

  b _____ up a business in another country is not an easy thing to do!

2 a I never _____ up for 9 o'clock lectures …

  b … it _____ out to be a great success.

3 a I was actually _____ forward to meeting new people …

  b I haven't _____ back!

4 a … no one _____ any fuss about it.

  b … it's the best decision I've ever _____ .

b Match the extracts in exercise **3a** to the following meanings.

0 There's a lot to learn and understand.   _There's a lot to get your head round._

1 I've never made a better decision.   _____

2 Nobody worried about it.   _____

3 It's difficult to start a company abroad.   _____

4 It was very successful in the end.   _____

5 I have become even more successful.   _____

116

2 High energy

(Listening Part 2) **Sentence completion** **1.6**

1 You will hear someone giving a talk about sports psychology. For questions **1–10**, complete the sentences with a word or short phrase.

The speaker says that as a schoolboy he had no **(1)** ....

Matthew Syed was an Olympic® **(2)** ....

According to Syed, we need to practise for about **(3)** .... hours to become a successful sportsperson or musician.

Tiger Woods started learning golf when he was **(4)** .... years old.

Success in sport becomes more difficult at a later age due to the number of **(5)** .... we have.

Many successful players came from Syed's **(6)** ....

Syed attributes his own success to having a particularly good **(7)** ....

Andre Agassi has written a book entitled **(8)** ....

Syed had a bad sporting experience in **(9)** ....

Some sports stars depend a great deal on **(10)** .... to cope with the pressure of competing.

2 The collocations in bold are from the listening. Complete the collocations with words from the box. You need to use two of the words twice.

for   in   on   to

1 It was really humiliating not to be **picked** _____ **a team** when I was at school.

2 My parents' encouragement **played a** big **part** _____ helping me to keep training regularly.

3 If you don't **put** _____ **the hours** you won't get anywhere in sport.

4 Lucy loves the idea of playing the flute but **when it comes** _____ practising she's not so keen!

5 A lot of young people train hard to become swimmers but only a very few **make it** _____ **the very top**.

6 Seb Coe is a former Olympic® champion but **he went** _____ **to** be a very important person in the organizing of the Olympic® Games in London in 2012.

3 A change for the better?

Listening **Part 4**) **Multiple choice** 👁 1.7

1 You will hear a man talking on a radio programme about changes he has noticed in his home town. For questions **1–7**, choose the best answer (**A**, **B** or **C**).

1 Tommy has not returned to his home town for a long time because

A he has had to devote all his time to acting.

B there are some aspects of his life there he is ashamed of.

C he no longer has close relatives in the area.

2 What contributed most to the changes in Tommy's attitude to life?

A becoming a celebrity

B being a long way from home

C not having his friends around him

3 How has the centre of Tommy's home town changed?

A The shops there are much bigger.

B It offers more facilities for families.

C The road system has altered.

4 How does Tommy feel about the changes made to the road where he used to live?

A He regrets the loss of green spaces.

B He is concerned about overcrowding in the area.

C He is full of admiration for the design of the new buildings.

5 What did Tommy use to do in his free time?

A Walk other people's dogs for them.

B Meet up with his friends outside the shops.

C Do open-air sporting activities.

6 Why did Tommy's parents want him to join the drama group?

A They thought it would keep him out of trouble.

B They felt he had real acting talent.

C They wanted to pass on their love of the theatre.

7 What does Tommy say he has heard about his old school?

A The sports facilities have improved.

B People think more highly of it now.

C The students are more involved in looking after the gardens.

2 Match the phrasal verbs in extracts **1–6** from the listening to the meanings **a–f**. The meanings are in the infinitive form.

1 Tommy Wells, the famous TV and film star, is a local boy who **grew up** in Marchwood.

2 Most of the mates I really valued **moved on**, like me.

3 I don't think I was a very nice person at that time. But I **grew out of it**, luckily!

4 [The houses have] all been **knocked down** and replaced with boring blocks of flats and retirement homes!

5 We used to **hang out** in the local park and practise our football skills.

6 My English teacher … pushed me to join the local drama group. I must admit I wasn't too keen – I'd rather have been **chilling out** with my mates!

a demolish

b spend time in a particular place (informal)

c change from being a baby or young child to being an older child or adult

d stop behaving in a certain way because you are older

e spend time relaxing (informal)

f leave one place to go to another

4 A good story

Listening Part 1) **Multiple choice** **1.8–1.15**

You will hear people talking in eight different situations. For questions **1–8**, choose the best answer (**A**, **B** or **C**).

1 You hear a woman talking about telling jokes. What does she say is her problem?

    A She cannot remember jokes.

    B She does not hear or read many jokes.

    C She cannot make people laugh.

2 You hear a man talking about writing books. What is he proud of?

    A He started writing at a young age.

    B He has adapted to writing on a computer.

    C He has published two books.

3 You hear two people talking about children's books. Where are they?

    A in a bookshop

    B at school

    C at home

4 You hear two people talking about a new drama series. How does the man feel about it?

    A disappointed

    B impressed

    C confused

5 You hear a voicemail message about a new job. What is the speaker doing?

    A making a recommendation

    B making an offer

    C making a request

6 You hear a woman talking about a lie she told. Why did she tell the lie?

    A her mum did not like her friends

    B she was bored with swimming

    C she needed the money

7 You hear two people talking about a writing competition. Why is the man concerned?

    A He wrote about the wrong topic.

    B He wrote his entry too quickly.

    C He sent his entry in too late.

8 You hear a voicemail message. What is the woman complaining about?

    A missing tickets

    B a replaced actor

    C inadequate booking arrangements

5 Doing what you have to

Listening **Part 2** **Sentence completion** 👁 **1.16**

1 You will hear author Sara James giving a talk about her work. For questions **1–10**, complete the sentences with a word or short phrase.

According to Sara, an essential requirement for a successful writer is **(1)** ....

Her first published book was called **(2)** ....

Before her first book was accepted she received **(3)** .... rejections.

Sara says she needs to have the same **(4)** .... every day.

Sara only writes in the **(5)** ....

She sometimes gets inspiration when she is in a **(6)** ....

Sara uses a **(7)** .... when she is writing the first draft of a story.

She has experience of getting **(8)** .... before a deadline.

She recommends writers do a **(9)** .... activity when they are stuck for ideas.

The initial plan was for **(10)** .... writers to participate in a documentary.

2 Complete the extracts from the listening with the correct form of a verb from the box.

fool go set write put run

1 Unless you have a lot of confidence in your book it might _____ some writers off.

2 Don't be _____ into believing that it's a glamorous or romantic life.

3 I _____ aside four hours every morning for writing.

4 I find that I work better if I _____ out my first drafts the old-fashioned way.

5 I'm afraid I've _____ out of time today.

6 A new documentary about different writers and their working lives will _____ out on Channel 3 next month.

6 Relative relationships

Listening Part 3 **Multiple matching** 1.17–1.21

1 You will hear five short extracts in which people are talking about their families. For questions **1–5**, choose from the list **A–H** what each speaker says about the different family members. Use the letters only once. There are three extra letters which you do not need to use.

A she has a busy working life with little opportunity to go out much

B she has worked hard to achieve her ambitions

C her marriage was not as strong as it seemed

D she now has the job that her parents had hoped for her

E she does not judge me

F she studied the same subject as the speaker

G she has a successful and steady relationship with her partner

H her work seems unsuited to her personality

Speaker 1	1
Speaker 2	2
Speaker 3	3
Speaker 4	4
Speaker 5	5

2 Match the phrases in bold in extracts **1–6** from the listening to the meanings **a–f**.

1 But she seemed to **prove them all wrong**.

2 Apparently they'd been **having an affair** for the previous five years.

3 Susan was devastated and **went to pieces** for about six months.

4 She'd always loved the open air and animals but she'd never wanted to **let anyone down**.

5 She's ten years older than me and I've always **looked up to her**.

6 She's also **pushed herself to the limit** to reach the top in her chosen sport.

a became extremely upset

b done as much as she possibly could

c show everyone they were mistaken

d admired and respected her

e going out with each other

f disappoint people

121

7 Value for money

Listening Part 4) **Multiple choice** **1.22**

You will hear part of a radio interview with a woman called Gail Simpson, who lives in an area where trees are protected. For questions **1–7**, choose the best answer (**A**, **B** or **C**).

1 Gail believes that people

   A cut down trees for building and furniture too easily.

   B do not spend enough time in the countryside.

   C do not think trees are an important subject.

2 Gail's main concern is related to

   A clean air.

   B quality of life.

   C money.

3 What do Gail and her husband like about the position of their house?

   A It is near woodland.

   B It is near the sea.

   C It is near a tourist attraction.

4 Why have the trees in her area been protected?

   A to stop them becoming extinct

   B to help maintain a natural habitat

   C to prevent new building projects

5 When did the tree disappear from Gail's garden?

   A during the night

   B during the tourist season

   C while Gail was on holiday

6 Why did Gail's neighbour want her to cut the tree down?

   A He thought it was dangerous.

   B It was too expensive for him to cut down himself.

   C He wanted his house to be worth more.

7 What has the neighbour done since the court case?

   A He has refused to speak to Gail and her husband.

   B He has moved away.

   C He has apologized.

Scots Pine

8 Up and away

Listening Part 1) **Multiple choice** **1.23–1.30**

You will hear people talking in eight different situations. For questions **1–8**, choose the best answer (**A**, **B** or **C**).

1 You hear a woman talking about a recent holiday.
  How did she feel when she heard about it?

  A annoyed

  B surprised

  C panicky

2 You hear someone talking about an upgrade on a flight.
  Why was it unexpected?

  A It had already happened once before.

  B There were a lot of people to choose from.

  C The speaker was not dressed very smartly.

3 You hear someone talking about a tourist sight.
  Who is the speaker?

  A a coach driver

  B a coach tour guide

  C a coach passenger

4 You hear someone talking about meeting a famous person.
  What does the speaker say about the famous person?

  A She was more attractive than he had thought.

  B She was shorter than he had thought.

  C She was shyer than he had thought.

5 You hear two people talking about a new car.
  What does the woman do in the conversation?

  A make a request

  B offer congratulations

  C make an apology

6 You hear someone talking about commuting to work every day.
  What does he dislike about it?

  A the crowded trains

  B getting up early

  C the cost

7 You hear someone talking on the radio.
  What is she advertising?

  A a type of holiday

  B a competition

  C a radio programme

8 You hear someone talking about taking the school bus when he was at school.
  What did he enjoy about it?

  A He felt grown up.

  B It saved time.

  C It was convenient.

9 Mystery and imagination

Sentence completion **1.31**

1 You will hear someone giving a talk about the famous writer Sir Arthur Conan Doyle.
For questions **1–10**, complete the sentences with a word or short phrase.

The speaker remembers reading one of Conan Doyle's **(1)** .... stories when he was young.

The first Sherlock Holmes story appeared in **(2)** ....

Conan Doyle lived and worked in the south-east of **(3)** ....

The person who had the most effect on Doyle's writing was his **(4)** ....

Sherlock Holmes is the hero in **(5)** .... of Conan Doyle's short stories.

Recent TV series about Sherlock Holmes take place in the **(6)** ....

Sherlock Holmes dies in the story **(7)** ....

Conan Doyle belonged to an organization called **(8)** ....

Conan Doyle wrote a famous **(9)** .... about a young girl who had supposedly photographed herself with fairies.

Initially, Conan Doyle's body was buried in the **(10)** .... at his home.

2 Complete the extracts from the listening with a word or phrase from the box.

| although   as well as   both   eventually   however   the time   when |

1 I was nine years old _____ I was captivated by the book *The Lost World*.

2 The stories of Sherlock Holmes have _____ delighted readers and inspired many crime writers.

3 By _____ he died in 1930 he had written … four novels about the famous detective. _____ , his writing was not restricted to stories about his most famous character.

4 _____ reading about him, we can also see Sherlock Holmes in many films and TV series.

5 _____ the Sherlock Holmes stories were very successful, Conan Doyle's real love was history.

6 He killed his famous detective … but his readers complained and _____ he brought Sherlock back.

10 Nothing but the truth

Multiple choice **1.32**

You will hear part of a radio interview with a man called Thomas Barker, who is an ex-criminal. For questions **1–7**, choose the best answer (**A**, **B** or **C**).

1 What does Thomas say about his home life when he was a child?

A His family had a lot of money.

B His parents were good role models.

C His brothers got into trouble with the police.

2 Thomas says that he started stealing things because

A he liked the element of danger.

B he wanted to be part of the group.

C he enjoyed getting things for free.

3 What was different about the crimes he was involved in later?

A the degree of planning

B the worry about getting caught

C the number of crimes he committed

4 What was Thomas' attitude to his crimes at that time?

A He did not take his crimes seriously.

B He disliked the level of violence involved.

C He envied the more serious criminals.

5 What was his reaction to being in prison?

A He enjoyed making new friends.

B He was confused about the reason for being there.

C He accepted the consequences of his actions.

6 When Thomas left prison he felt

A angry with his parents for not accommodating him.

B concerned that he might reoffend and return to prison.

C grateful to the prison for the opportunities it had given him.

7 Thomas works today to

A help prisoners to rehabilitate.

B help the police to detect crime.

C help others to avoid the problems that he had.

11 What on earth's going on?

Listening Part 1 **Multiple choice** 1.33–1.40

You will hear people talking in eight different situations. For questions **1–8**, choose the best answer (**A**, **B** or **C**).

1 You hear a man talking about his work. Why did he change his job?

  A He wanted to do outdoor work.

  B He had health problems.

  C He needed more money.

2 You hear a man telling someone about getting lost. How did he feel about getting lost?

  A scared

  B excited

  C annoyed

3 You hear two people talking at a zoo. How does the woman feel?

  A worried

  B sad

  C bored

4 You hear a woman talking about a sport. Why might she give it up?

  A It takes up too much time.

  B It is too expensive.

  C The weather is getting too bad.

5 You hear a voicemail message. Who is the woman?

  A a mother

  B a colleague

  C a friend

6 You hear a man talking about recent flooding. What does he want the council to do?

  A to keep their promise to stop future flooding

  B to pay the people for the damage the water caused

  C to apologize to the people affected by the flooding

7 You hear the following on the radio. What is it from?

  A a weather forecast

  B a health programme

  C a local news programme

8 You hear a woman talking to her friend. What is she doing?

  A complaining about something

  B offering to do something

  C giving advice about something

12 Looking after yourself

Multiple matching 👁 1.41–1.45

1 You will hear five short extracts in which people are talking about cooking. For questions **1–5**, choose from the list **A–H** what each speaker says. There are three extra letters which you do not need to use.

A My mother taught me everything I know about cooking.

B I had some bad experiences which put me off cooking.

C I learnt to cook because I needed to.

D I have problems with my cooking because my equipment is not reliable.

E I cook the sort of meals that are not popular with everyone.

F I handed over the cooking to another member of my family.

G I was trained to cook by a celebrity chef.

H I learnt that you need to be patient when you are cooking.

Speaker 1 ⬜ 1
Speaker 2 ⬜ 2
Speaker 3 ⬜ 3
Speaker 4 ⬜ 4
Speaker 5 ⬜ 5

2a Complete the sentences with the correct form of a verb from the box. The words and phrases in bold were used by the speakers in the listening.

get (x2)   look   make   turn   work

1 It can be quite a shock when you leave home and have to start _____ **after** yourself.

2 I've got a lot of emails to answer. I'm _____ **my way through** them quite quickly but I won't be finished for another hour.

3 I've been playing this new computer game for hours but I just can't _____ **the hang of** it.

4 I overslept this morning but I _____ **up** an excuse and told my boss that the trains were all delayed.

5 I was quite worried about the project I did last week because I rushed it a bit, but luckily it _____ **out** well. The teacher loved it.

6 I _____ **fed up with** my diet so I'm back to eating normally now!

b Match the meanings **a–f** to the words and phrases in bold in exercise **2a**.

a learn how to do _____get the hang of_____

b became tired of _____

c invented _____

d taking care of _____

e gradually dealing with _____

f had a particular result _____

13 Animal magic

Sentence completion 1.46

1 You will hear someone giving a talk about pavement art. For questions **1–10**, complete the sentences with a word or short phrase.

Many paintings are not seen by the public because they are kept in **(1)** ....

The only way to keep pavement art for more than a few days is in **(2)** ....

Pavement art is becoming more familiar to people today thanks to **(3)** ....

The speaker says that Edgar Mueller's 3D pavement art is very **(4)** ....

Italian artists first started to paint pictures on pavements in **(5)** ....

These artists also painted pictures in **(6)** ....

There were a lot fewer pavement artists after the **(7)** ....

The famous English pavement artist Julian Beever had a nickname based on the famous painter **(8)** ....

Mueller first won a street art competition when he was **(9)** ....

The biggest pavement art festival in the world is in **(10)** ....

2 Complete the sentences with the correct adjectival form of words from the box.

complicate	influence	prestige	real	religion	three-dimension	tradition

1 The explanation was very _____ and I couldn't understand it.

2 Most people in my town are quite _____ and go to church regularly.

3 Salvador Dali was a very _____ painter and many artists have been inspired by his work.

4 Your picture isn't very _____ ! It doesn't look anything like your sister.

5 I love folk songs played on _____ instruments.

6 Winners of the _____ Pulitzer Prize for fiction become internationally famous.

7 In 2012 they started making a _____ film version of *The Hobbit* by J.R.R. Tolkien.

14 Mind your language

Listening
Part 3

Multiple matching 1.47–1.51

1 You will hear five people talking about surviving difficult situations. For questions **1–5**, choose from the list **A–H** what each speaker says. Use the letters only once. There are three extra letters which you do not need to use.

A I still do not know what caused my problem.

B I was unable to work because I became very sick.

C I lost my job because I could not deal with my problems.

D My problem was a result of my unrealistic expectations.

E I did not realize the seriousness of my situation at the time.

F I nearly died while I was on holiday.

G I was fortunate to have the support of a family member.

H Meeting new people helped me at a difficult time in my life.

Speaker 1 ☐ 1
Speaker 2 ☐ 2
Speaker 3 ☐ 3
Speaker 4 ☐ 4
Speaker 5 ☐ 5

2 Match the phrasal verbs in bold from the listening to the meanings **a–f**.

1 I prefer to work independently rather than have to **answer to** other people.

2 I **struggled to cope with** my university exams so I delayed taking them for another year.

3 In my interview **my mind went completely blank** and I felt stupid.

4 I thought I'd met Robin before but I **couldn't trust my memory**.

5 Some people **can't handle the pressure** of a high-powered job.

6 Seeing the boy was upset, the shopkeeper **took pity on** him and gave him a sweet.

a was unsure if I had remembered correctly

b justify my actions to

c found it difficult to deal with

d felt sorry for

e find something too stressful

f I couldn't remember anything

Phrasal verb list

be given over to something (5)	use something for a particular purpose
be made up of something (2)	consist of; be composed of
be taken up with something (5)	be busy doing something
bolt something down (12)	eat food very quickly
branch out (13)	start doing something new or different
bring someone up (6)	take care of a child until they become an adult
call someone out (5)	ask a person or organization that provides a service to come and deal with something for you
carry out* something (9/12/13)	do a piece of work or research
catch on (8)	begin to understand
clear something up (5)	make a place tidy
come across something/ someone (8)	find/meet someone/something by chance
come in for criticism (13)	receive criticism
come over (10)	visit someone in their house
come up with an idea (8)	think of
eat up* something (12)	eat all of something
end up (somewhere) (2)	be in a particular place, after or because of something
fall for someone (6)	fall in love with someone
fall out with someone (6)	stop being friendly with someone because you have had an argument or disagreement with them
find something out (3/10)	discover
get about (a place) (8)	travel around
get away with something (10)	manage to do something bad without being punished or criticized for it
get by (1)	manage to survive/live
get on (3)	progress
get on with someone (6)	have a good relationship with someone
get out of (doing) something (10)	avoid doing something that you should do
get over someone (6)	start to forget someone and feel happy again after a relationship has ended
get over something (1)	recover from
get through something (5)	pass a test or stage of something
give away* information (9)	tell information that should be kept secret
give homework in (9)	hand homework to the teacher
give in (to someone's requests) (9)	agree to something after initial resistance

give off* a smell (9)	produce and send into the air
give oneself up (9)	allow oneself to be arrested by the police
give out* (books/paper) (9)	give something to several people
give out* information (9)	give information to a lot of people
give something back (9)	return something
give something up (5/9)	stop doing something you do regularly
go ahead (3)	take action, proceed
go away (to somewhere) (8)	go on holiday
go on (3)	happen
go on to do something (5)	do something after you have finished doing something else
go out with someone (6)	have a romantic relationship with someone
grow up (6)	change from being a baby or young child to being an older child or adult
gulp something down (12)	swallow/drink very quickly
hand over to someone (5)	to give power, control or responsibility to someone else
head for somewhere (8)	go somewhere
head off (in search of something) (7)	leave somewhere (to go and look for something)
let someone down (6)	disappoint
look forward to something (1)	feel happy about something that is going to happen
look up to someone (6)	admire and respect
make something up (10)	invent
make up one's mind (14)	make a decision
nod off (8)	go to sleep
open up to someone (10)	talk more about your personal feelings
own up to someone (10)	admit that you have done something wrong
put a book down (11)	stop reading
put a team/crew together (11)	assemble a group of people
put an event off (11)	postpone
put clothes on (11)	place on your body
put on* an event (11)	organize
put prices up (11)	increase
put someone off (11)	distract
put someone off (doing) (8/11)	discourage something
put someone through something (7)	make someone experience something difficult or unpleasant
put someone up (for the night) (11)	accommodate
put something out (5)	make something stop burning, extinguish
put the radio/TV on (11)	make equipment start working
put up with something/someone (6/7/8/11)	tolerate something/someone
put weight on (11)	gain
put your feet up (11)	relax
put your hand up (11)	raise into the air
run into (problems) (2)	begin to experience
run out of something (2/10)	use all of something so that none is left
show off (10)	behave in a way intended to attract people's attention and make them admire you

sleep in (8)	continue sleeping after the time you usually get up
sort out* a problem (6)	deal with a problem
speak out (3)	say firmly and publicly what you think
split up with someone (3/6)	end a romantic relationship with someone
take after someone (4)	resemble
take off (4)	start to become successful
take on a challenge (13)	accept
take over (4)	gain control
take someone aside (4)	move away from other people to talk
take someone on (4)	employ
take something in (4)	accept as true
take to something/someone (4)	start to like
take up* a new sport/hobby (4)	start doing
team up with someone (2)	join with other people in order to do something
tell someone off (6)	criticize someone angrily for doing something wrong
turn back (14)	return instead of continuing
turn into something (14)	change or develop into
turn off (a road) (14)	leave one road to take another
turn out (14)	become known
turn out (8)	attend/take part in an event
turn someone down (14)	reject
turn something off (14)	stop something working
turn something over (14)	turn something to see the other side
turn the volume up (14)	increase the volume
turn to someone (6)	go to someone for help
turn up (14)	arrive in a way that was not planned

Lexical phrase list

do (Unit 14)

do a course
do a degree
do a job
do an exercise
do some exercise
do nothing but
do some research
do someone a favour
do the housework
do the ironing/shopping/washing/
washing up
do badly/better/well/worse
do your best
do your homework
I/it could do with something
it will/would do someone good/no
harm to do something
it has something to do with

get (Unit 1)

get angry/upset/bored/lonely, etc.
get a cold/headache/the flu, etc.
get a job (5)
get a nose bleed (12)
get (back) home
get better/worse/older, etc.
get engaged/married/divorced
get (some) exercise
get in touch with someone
get in/out of a car/taxi
get into trouble (with the police)
get into/out of the habit of doing
something
get on/off a bus/train/plane
get on someone's nerves
get one's head round something
get paid
get promoted/transferred/sacked
get ready (for work/school/
Christmas)
get rid of something/someone
get someone to do something
get something for Christmas/your
birthday
get something from a shop
get the bus/train/plane
get the chance to do something

get the hang of something (12)
get the impression that
get the dinner ready
get to do something
get to school/work/a place
get to sleep (8)
get used to doing something

give (Unit 9)

give a broad smile
give a concert
give a deep sigh
give a lengthy speech
give a nervous laugh
give a party
give a piercing scream
give an example
give an impressive performance
give me great pleasure
give someone a blank look
give someone a call
give someone a hand
give someone an idea
give someone an injection (12)
give someone a lift
give someone a nasty shock
give someone a pleasant surprise
give someone a prescription (12)
give someone a tender kiss
give someone advice
give someone full details
give someone my best regards
give someone permission to do
something
give someone the impression that

make (Unit 14)

make a complaint
make a decision
make a good/bad impression
make a living
make a mess (of something)
make a mistake
make a noise
make a phone call
make a speech
make an appointment

make an arrangement
make an effort
make friends with someone
make fun of someone
make it to the top (2)
make progress
make sure
make up your mind

put (Unit 11)

put (a lot of) time/effort/
hard work/energy into (doing)
something
put a plaster on a cut (12)
put a CD/DVD on
put one's feet up
put pressure on someone (to do
something)
put some money aside
put someone's arm in plaster (12)
put someone/someone's health/life
at risk
put someone in a good mood
put someone on a course of
antibiotics (12)
put someone up for the night
put the blame on someone for
(doing) something
I can't/couldn't put my book down

take (Unit 4)

take ages/a long time to do
something
take a joke
take a photo
take a risk
take a turn for the worse (14)
take care of
take (a keen) interest in
take notice of
take offence at
take part in something (2)
take pity on
take place (2)
take pride in
take some medicine/a pill (12)
take someone to a restaurant/out
for a meal

Lexical phrase list

take someone to school/hospital/work

take someone's advice

take someone's temperature (12)

take something back to a shop

take someone/something seriously

take the blame for

take the infinitive/gerund

take time to do something

it takes courage to do something

turn (Unit 14)

at the turn of the century

turn 30/40, etc.

turn a blind eye to something

turn blue/green, etc.

turn to page 20

turn out well (12)

it's my/your, etc. turn to do something

one good turn deserves another

Irregular verb list

Infinitive	Past simple	Past participle
arise	arose	arisen
awake	awoke	awoken
be	was/were	been
bear	bore	borne
beat	beat	beaten
become	became	become
begin	began	begun
bend	bent	bent
bet	bet	bet
bind	bound	bound
bite	bit	bitten
blow	blew	blown
break	broke	broken
breed	bred	bred
bring	brought	brought
build	built	built
burn	burnt/burned	burnt/burned
burst	burst	burst
buy	bought	bought
catch	caught	caught
choose	chose	chosen
come	came	come
cost	cost	cost
creep	crept	crept
cut	cut	cut
deal	dealt	dealt
dig	dug	dug
do	did	done
draw	drew	drawn
dream	dreamt/dreamed	dreamt/dreamed
drink	drank	drunk
drive	drove	driven
eat	ate	eaten
fall	fell	fallen
feed	fed	fed
feel	felt	felt
fight	fought	fought
find	found	found
flee	fled	fled
fly	flew	flown
forbid	forbade	forbidden
forget	forgot	forgotten
forgive	forgave	forgiven
freeze	froze	frozen
get	got	got/gotten (AE)
give	gave	given
go	went	gone
grind	ground	ground
grow	grew	grown
hang	hung	hung

Irregular verb list

Infinitive	Past simple	Past participle
have	had	had
hear	heard	heard
hide	hid	hidden
hit	hit	hit
hold	held	held
hurt	hurt	hurt
keep	kept	kept
kneel	knelt	knelt
know	knew	known
lay	laid	laid
lead	led	led
lean	leant/leaned	leant/leaned
learn	learnt/learned	learnt/learned
leave	left	left
lend	lent	lent
let	let	let
lie	lay	lain
light	lit	lit
lose	lost	lost
make	made	made
mean	meant	meant
meet	met	met
pay	paid	paid
put	put	put
seek	sought	sought
show	showed	shown
shrink	shrank/shrunk	shrunk
slide	slid	slid
smell	smelt/smelled	smelt/smelled
sow	sowed	sown
speed	sped	sped
spill	spilt/spilled	spilt/spilled
spin	spun	spun
spit	spat	spat
split	split	split
spoil	spoilt/spoiled	spoilt/spoiled
spread	spread	spread
spring	sprang	sprung
sting	stung	stung
stink	stank/stunk	stunk
strike	struck	struck
swear	swore	sworn
sweep	swept	swept
swell	swelled	swollen/swelled
swing	swung	swung
take	took	taken
tread	trod	trodden
weave	wove	woven
weep	wept	wept
wind	wound	wound

Answer key

Unit 1 Lifestyle

Reading and Use of English: Multiple matching, pages 4–5

1

1 B 2 A 3 B 4 C 5 D 6 A 7 D 8 C 9 B
10 A

2

1 side 2 nerves 3 feet, end 4 place 5 holiday
6 lifestyle 7 own 8 shows

3

b on my own
c on our feet for hours on end
d get on each other's nerves
e putting on shows
f go on with this lifestyle

Vocabulary, pages 6–7

A Lifestyle

1 healthy 2 luxurious 3 chaotic 4 sedentary
5 alternative

B Clothes

1

1 scruffy 2 scarf 3 casual 4 tight 5 plain
6 socks 7 trainers 8 baggy 9 belt 10 helmet
11 bracelet 12 fashionable

2

1 a pleated skirt 2 a checked waistcoat
3 a flowery dress 4 striped swimming trunks
5 spotted socks

C *Get*

1

1 by 2 over 3 back 4 away 5 off 6 out of

2

1 touch 2 paid 3 rid 4 ready 5 worse
6 impression 7 exercise

D Word combinations

1

1 party 2 interview 3 event 4 premiere 5 life

2

1 sporting event 2 social life 3 dinner jacket
4 world premiere 5 radio interview 6 political
party

Language focus, page 8

A Adverbs of frequency

1 I always set my alarm clock
2 I am never late

3 I rarely drink it
4 My mum cooks paella once a week
5 we have never been to Paris

B *Be used to*, *get used to* and *used to*

1 Lucy used to use a bike to get to school.
2 She's got used to getting up early in the
  morning.
3 My dad used to get me to clean his car every
  Sunday.
4 Paul didn't use to get paid much when he
  worked as a waiter.
5 Many young people are not used to doing hard
  work.

Reading and Use of English: Transformations, page 8

1 hardly ever stay/am hardly ever
2 used to getting
3 looking forward to going
4 has/'s taken (me) so
5 is/'s rare for Anna to
6 not like Richard/him to be

Reading and Use of English: Multiple-choice cloze, page 9

1 A 2 C 3 D 4 C 5 B 6 D 7 A 8 C

Writing: Informal letter and email, pages 10–11

1

	Formal	Informal
Complaining	7	4
Asking for information	1	10
Giving information	5	9
Apologizing	3	6
Giving advice	8	2

2

Formal	Informal
1 inform me	10 let me know
8 We strongly advise you not to	2 You really shouldn't
3 for the delay in responding to you	6 it's taken me so long to get back to you
7 Moreover	4 And
5 I have a wide range of experience in working	9 I've done loads of jobs in hotels

Informal letter

2

Paragraph 1 a   Paragraph 2 c   Paragraph 3 b

Unit 2 High energy

Reading and Use of English: Gapped text, pages 12–15

1

1 C 2 F 3 A 4 E 5 G 6 B D not used

2

1 head 2 eye 3 foot 4 arm 5 mouth 6 face

Vocabulary, pages 13–15

A Music

1
1 trumpet 2 flute 3 violin 4 tambourine
5 drum 6 saxophone 7 keyboard 8 accordion

2
1 song 2 wind 3 charts 4 lead 5 session
6 tune

B Sport

1

a athlete b basketball player c cyclist d golfer
e gymnast f skier g snowboarder h tennis
player

2

2 football pitch 3 athletics track 4 ski slope
5 swimming pool 6 golf course 7 tennis court
8 ice-skating rink

3

1 B 2 D 3 A 4 C 5 C 6 D 7 A 8 B

C

Word formation

1 irrelevant 2 disagreement 3 misunderstood
4 dishonestly 5 unreliable 6 immature
7 overweight 8 undercooked 9 irresponsibly
10 incapable

Language focus, pages 15–16

A Indirect ways of asking questions

1 telling me what you have been doing recently
2 where I can get something cold to drink
3 what time you are coming to the party next
   week
4 to me why you did not do the homework
5 if you are interested in playing tennis on
   Friday
6 what he does for a living

B Gerunds and infinitives

1 looking, to have
2 learning, to speak, to think
3 to be, climbing, attracting, to wait
4 making, to concentrate
5 going, to stay
6 Giving, to lose/losing
7 to hear, seeing
8 to paint, forgetting, to buy

9 to live, to find, to pay
10 to work, going

C Open cloze: Prepositions

1 in 2 on 3 in 4 in 5 on 6 on 7 at 8 in
9 in 10 at 11 with 12 until/to

Reading and Use of English: Transformations, page 17

1 help laughing
2 feel like going
3 didn't/did not deserve to lose
4 to prevent people (from) recognizing
5 didn't/did not mean to shoot
6 can't/cannot stand being

Reading and Use of English: Multiple-choice cloze, page 17

1 B 2 D 3 B 4 A 5 C 6 C 7 D 8 D

Writing: Formal letter, pages 18–19

A Formal and informal style
1 b 2 b 3 a 4 a 5 b 6 a 7 b 8 b 9 a 10 b

B A formal letter
5 b, 8 b (new paragraph); 3 a, 1 b, 10 b (new
paragraph); 9 a, 2 b, 6 a (new paragraph);
7 b, 4 a

Dear Ms Appleby

(5b) I am writing in reply to your request for
information on dance shows which your students could
see during their visit here next month. (8b) There is a
wide range of shows to choose from, but there are two
which I believe would be of particular interest to your
students.

(3a) Firstly, the popular Irish dance troupe 'Rhythm
of the Dance' will be performing here for the fourth
time in five years. (1b) I saw them on all three previous
occasions and would certainly recommend going to see
this latest show. (10b) It includes their usual mixture of
traditional dance and music, but combines it, this time
apparently, with up-to-date stage technology.

(9a) Another option which sounds enjoyable is the
all-male Australian tap dance group, 'Tap Dogs'. (2b)
According to the publicity, the show combines the
strength and power of workmen with the precision
and talent of tap dancing. (6a) In addition, the six
Australians dance on water during the performance,
splashing members of the audience in the front rows.

(7b) I feel certain your students would enjoy either of
the shows I have described. (4a) If you would like any
further information, please do not hesitate to contact
me.

Yours sincerely

Rita Kuyper

Unit 3 A change for the better?

Reading and Use of English: Multiple matching, pages 20–21

1

a A, B, D

b C, E

2

1 A **2** C **3** B **4** E **5** D **6** C **7** A **8** E **9** B
10 A

3

a takes up **b** bring up **c** comes out **d** get by
e moved on

4

1 get by **2** came out **3** takes up
4 brought (me) up **5** moved on

Vocabulary, page 22

Technology

Across	Down
1 laughing	**1** laptop
4 remote	**2** by the way
6 download	**3** multitask
9 information	**5** handheld
11 textspeak	**7** handsfree
14 landline	**8** out
15 browse	**10** on
16 log	**12** personal
17 headset	**13** opinion

Language focus, pages 23–24

A Articles

1 The, a, –, the

2 –, the, a

3 a, a, the, The, a

4 –, –, the, an, an, a, –, the

5 the, –, a, an

B Comparisons

1

1 hard **2** hottest **3** more careful **4** better
5 cold **6** most boring **7** more tired/tireder
8 earlier **9** fastest **10** quieter/more quiet

2

1 d **2** e **3** a **4** b **5** h **6** c **7** f **8** g

C Correcting mistakes

1

1 Walkman **2** compass **3** video **4** space
blanket **5** radar

2

1

This invention <u>which</u> completely changed
But <u>however</u> its creator

the portable device, <u>more</u> smaller than a
paperback book

2

This device was the most <u>of</u> important
to <u>can</u> know
the most significant <u>of</u> event

3

significantly <u>very</u> cheaper versions
nearly as <u>most</u> common
as <u>more</u> often as they liked

4

a type of <u>the</u> plastic
It is used <u>to</u>, for example
as a result of <u>the</u> man's efforts

5

and is used <u>for</u> to detect
as an instrument <u>as</u> of war
In addition <u>to</u>,

Reading and Use of English: Open cloze, page 24

1 for **2** are **3** on **4** not **5** to **6** it **7** who/that
8 be

Reading and Use of English: Word formation, page 25

1 ability **2** incomplete **3** inventor **4** later
5 appearance **6** electrician **7** improvement
8 popularity

Reading and Use of English: Transformations, page 25

1 thinner than he used to

2 not nearly as hard/difficult as

3 is the same size as

4 a lot of difference between

5 not as many girls

6 the cleverest person I have/I've

Writing: Article, pages 26–27

2

Paragraph 1: c
Paragraph 2: a
Paragraph 3: d
Paragraph 4: b
Possible title: A love-hate relationship

3

Contractions: couldn't, there's, didn't, aren't, it's,
can't, isn't
Phrasal verbs: live without, do without, get by

Linking words: but/But, and/And, Firstly, If, So
Direct questions: The first and last sentences of
the article.

Unit 4 A good story

Reading and Use of English: Multiple choice, pages 28–29

1

1 B 2 D 3 C 4 A 5 C 6 C

2

a seminal **b** dismissive **c** chilling **d** clumsy
e literate **f** trendy **g** lofty

Vocabulary, pages 30–31

A Cinema and films

1 cast 2 plot 3 makeup 4 scene 5 comedy
6 effects 7 part 8 stuntman 9 office
10 remake 11 soundtrack

B Expressions with *take*

1 interest 2 offence 3 pity 4 blame 5 care
6 notice 7 advice 8 joke 9 courage 10 risk

C Phrasal verbs with *take*

1 over 2 up 3 to 4 after 5 on 6 aside

D Word formation: Adjectives ending in *-ing* and *-ed*

1 frightening 2 embarrassed 3 increasingly
4 tiring, exhausted 5 uninteresting
6 surprisingly 7 confused
8 annoying, unconvincing, impressed

Language focus, pages 31–32

A Tenses

1

1 had been living, started, was training, met

2 heard, phoned, had got, told, had taken

3 were watching, went, had forgotten

4 got, had eaten, had already left, were still dancing

2

1 was working 2 had had 3 (had) agreed
4 was progressing 5 were talking
6 flew 7 landed 8 had, seen 9 picked 10 put
11 carried 12 had happened

B Linking words

1 for 2 As 3 In the end 4 at last 5 After

Reading and Use of English: Transformations, page 32

Part 4: Transformations

1 such a good

2 so interested in the book

3 does it take to

4 takes pride in

5 soon as we arrive at

6 it back at the end

Reading and Use of English: Multiple-choice cloze, page 33

1 C 2 C 3 A 4 D 5 D 6 C 7 B 8 A

Reading and Use of English: Open cloze, page 33

1 than 2 a/any 3 there 4 without 5 same
6 has 7 in 8 but

Writing: Essay, pages 34–35

1b

1

Paragraph 2: Advantages of books compared to film versions

Paragraph 3: Advantages of film versions compared to books

Paragraph 4: Conclusion: writer's opinion

2

The writer says that films are more memorable than books because they are more visual.

2b

1 Many ~~of~~ people

2 **On** the one hand

3 lasts ~~more~~ longer

4 what ~~do~~ the characters

5 the most **interesting** scenes

6 takes less effort **than** reading a novel

7 too tired to open **a** book

8 You may need **to read** a book

9 **it is always** better

10 if you want **to** compare

Unit 5 Doing what you have to

Reading and Use of English: Multiple matching, pages 36–37

1

1 E 2 B 3 A 4 D 5 B 6 C 7 E 8 A 9 D
10 E

2

1 scanner 2 calculator 3 adviser/advisor
4 inventor 5 presenter 6 demonstrator
7 competitor 8 photocopier 9 researcher
10 spectator

Vocabulary, pages 38–39

A Jobs

Across	Down
1 dustman	2 teacher
6 baker	3 waitress
8 hairdresser	4 lawyer
9 chef	5 butcher
11 accountant	7 surgeon
	10 vet

B Questions and answers

1

1 e **2** g **3** a **4** c **5** f **6** h **7** b **8** d

2

judge, politician, company director (other answers may be acceptable)

C Expressions with *work*

1 worked, overtime

2 to work long hours

3 working part-time, working full-time

4 to work flexitime

5 worked for myself

D Confusing words

1 resign **2** earn **3** set **4** apply **5** degree

Language focus, pages 39–40

A Noun phrases

1 Sunday's **2** bottom of the stairs **3** broken
4 postman, garden gate **5** cup of coffee
6 lack of confidence **7** month's **8** January

B Obligation, necessity and permission

1

1 should **2** let **3** mustn't, allowed, have
4 shouldn't **5** don't have, make **6** ought **7** had

2

1 shouldn't/must **2** can/can't **3** needn't/must
4 can/should **5** can't/must

Reading and Use of English: Multiple-choice cloze, page 40

1 A **2** D **3** A **4** B **5** C **6** C **7** B **8** D

Reading and Use of English: Open cloze, page 41

1 a **2** made **3** into **4** something **5** up **6** us
7 there **8** as

Reading and Use of English: Word formation, page 41

1 patience **2** ability **3** annoyed **4** confidence
5 Unfortunately **6** threatened **7** brightens
8 satisfying

Reading and Use of English: Transformations, page 42

1 you (will/'ll) have to put

2 are they supposed to

3 'd/had better not drink/have

4 ought to have/show more

5 will not/won't/do not/don't let me stay

6 was made to clean

Writing: Letter of application, pages 42–43

2

1 g **2** b, f, a, d **3** h, j **4** c, i **5** e

3

a sincerely **b** faithfully

Unit 6 Relative relationships

Reading and Use of English: Gapped text, pages 44–45

1

1 E **2** B **3** F **4** C **5** A **6** G

2

1 light,	S		
2 lives,	D	**a** /laivz/	**b** /livz/
3 spare,	S		
4 turn,	S		
5 contract,	D	**a** /ˈkɒntrækt/	
		b /kɒnˈtrækt/	
6 hard,	S		
7 mean,	S		
8 used,	D	**a** /juːst/	**b** /juːzd/
9 book,	S		
10 fair,	S		

Vocabulary, page 46

A Adjectives of personality

1

1 fussy **2** bossy **3** clumsy **4** stubborn **5** dull
6 reserved **7** ambitious **8** affectionate

2

1 selfish **2** unreliable **3** flowing **4** sensitive
5 indecisive **6** spotty **7** tolerant **8** impatient

Language focus, pages 46–48

A Causative passive

1 We had our car repaired yesterday.

2 I want to get my ears pierced.

3 She has (had) never had her teeth whitened before.

4 I'm getting (going to get) my hair cut at 5 o'clock tomorrow.

5 They'll probably have (They're probably going to have) their house painted next month.

6 I always have my suits made in Milan now.

B Phrasal verbs

1 a I'm very fond of my grandmother. I've always looked up to her.

2 a I think I take after my father rather than my mother.

3 b I don't earn a great deal but I get by.

4 a I blame the parents. They haven't brought him up very well.

5 b It was a tough interview but I think I got through it OK.

C Relative clauses

1 who, which

2 who/that, whose

3 where, which/that

4 why/that, when

5 which, where

6 who/that, which/that

7 which/that, which, whose

Commas are required in the following sentences:

1 after *Mr Jones* and *15 years*

4 after *January*

5 after *The fox*, *shy animal* and *residential areas*

7 after *on Friday* and *my eldest sister*

Reading and Use of English: Transformations, page 48

1 had our house broken into/had a break-in

2 to have my hair dyed

3 for whom I have

4 whose ruler I borrowed

5 look up to is

6 let them down

Reading and Use of English: Multiple-choice cloze, page 49

1 B **2** D **3** D **4** B **5** C **6** A **7** C **8** A

Reading and Use of English: Open cloze, page 49

1 whose **2** having **3** what **4** on **5** up **6** not
7 take **8** for

Writing: Essay, pages 50–51

1

1 The writer disagrees with the statement

2 b The writer offers only arguments which support his or her opinion.

2

Online forums and chats make it possible for parents to get help in understanding teenage children's problems.

3

Although, Firstly, Because, also, Moreover, Consequently, Finally, To sum up, If

Before you write

5

1 life as a single person: b, d, e

2 economic factors: a, c, f

6

Couple A: b, d, f

Couple B: a, c, e

Unit 7 Value for money

Reading and Use of English: Multiple matching, pages 52–53

1

1 B **2** D **3** A **4** C **5** B **6** A **7** B **8** D **9** C
10 A

2

1 d **2** f **3** e **4** b **5** a **6** c

3

1 turned into **2** put up with **3** moved out
4 springing up **5** cut down, cut out

4

1 I always refused to set foot in

2 I've had a moan at them

3 came to an agreement

4 put (my flat) up for sale

5 I'm on first-name terms with

6 I've got my eye on

Vocabulary, pages 53–55

A Shopping

1

T	T	T	S	I	R	O	L	F	G
F	R	T	I	I	E	A	E	R	C
R	O	N	G	L	L	A	O	G	H
E	L	E	O	F	I	C	E	R	E
T	L	G	O	I	E	H	L	E	C
N	E	A	D	R	W	E	S	H	K
U	Y	S	S	S	E	C	I	C	O
O	H	W	A	H	J	K	A	T	U
C	H	E	M	I	S	T	A	U	T
C	N	N	I	A	G	R	A	B	T

Shopkeepers: baker, butcher, chemist, florist, grocer, jeweller, newsagent

Things in shops or supermarkets: aisle, bargain, checkout, counter, goods, till, trolley

2

1 B **2** C **3** C **4** A **5** B **6** D **7** A **8** D **9** B
10 A

B Towns and villages

1

1 prosperous **2** bustling **3** run-down **4** quaint
5 depressing

2

1 block 2 street 3 site 4 area 5 estate

C Paraphrasing

1 in, for 2 for, of/about 3 to, about/of
4 of, from 5 for, of

Language focus, pages 55–56

A Present perfect simple, present perfect continuous and past simple

1 has increased, (were) expected, lived, has risen

2 have moved, have never stayed, sold, changed, have been moving

3 have known, have been trying, have phoned, has happened, went, seemed

4 has just walked, has been playing, made, has been going/has gone

5 retired, have been, have taken, laid, have been putting

B Correcting mistakes

1 My father's been working/has worked

2 I've broken my leg

3 Charlie Chaplin was one of the greatest

4 how long I've been waiting

5 the first time I have seen this film

6 known each other for many years

7 since I played football

8 I have cleaned three rooms

C Expressing preferences

1 to 2 rather 3 than 4 not 5 would 6 much

Reading and Use of English: Multiple-choice cloze, page 56

1 B 2 D 3 C 4 A 5 B 6 D 7 C 8 C

Reading and Use of English: Open cloze, page 57

1 as 2 in 3 within/in 4 no 5 been/stayed
6 since 7 up 8 on

Reading and Use of English: Word formation, page 57

1 picturesque 2 inhabitants 3 beautiful
4 pleasant 5 disadvantages 6 infrequent
7 dependent 8 unfriendly

Reading and Use of English: Transformations, page 58

1 is/has been a month since

2 last time we saw

3 not leave yet

4 to walk rather than catch

5 not to blame for

6 did not/didn't break into a

Writing: Review, pages 58–59

A Structure

Paragraph 1: d   Paragraph 2: a
Paragraph 3: c   Paragraph 4: b

B Language analysis

1

1 competitive, fast, efficient, useful, informative, handy, decent

2 extremely (competitive), particularly (useful), very (informative), fairly (good), especially (handy)

3 normally, always, sometimes, usually, often, already

2

1 about 2 fact 3 Personally 4 anyone

Unit 8 Up and away

Reading and Use of English: Multiple choice, pages 60–61

1

1 C 2 A 3 C 4 D 5 B 6 A

2

1 took up 2 catch up on 3 put off 4 used up
5 picked up

3

1 for, by, on

2 of, with, in, at, between

3 on, for

4 across, at, through, on

5 of, of, in

Vocabulary, page 62

A Travel

1 fun 2 crowded 3 campsite 4 holiday 5 stay
6 resort 7 souvenirs 8 views 9 trip 10 cruise

B Phrasal verbs

1 come across 2 turn out 3 get about 4 head for 5 catch on

C Sleep

1 taking 2 to stay 3 to fall 4 nodding
5 to sleep

Language focus, pages 63–64

The future

1

1 I'll put

2 you're going to have/you're (just) about to have/you're having

3 We're meeting/We're going to meet

4 you leave

5 I'll get/I'm going to get

6 we'll be sitting

7 are you doing/are you going to do

8 I'll have spoken

2

1 'll/will carry

2 'm/am having/going to have

3 ends, 'll/will be

4 'll/will be watching, 'll/will have finished

5 'm/am going to get

6 gets/has got

7 'll/will have been travelling, 'll/will want

8 'll be/'m going to be

3

1 until, finish/have finished 2 after, sets/has set
3 as, stops 4 when/after, say 5 By, get

Reading and Use of English: Multiple-choice cloze, page 64

1 C 2 A 3 D 4 C 5 B 6 C 7 A 8 A

Reading and Use of English: Open cloze, page 65

1 a/each/every/per 2 well 3 than 4 with 5 is
6 which 7 whose 8 one

Reading and Use of English: Word formation, page 65

1 congratulations 2 fascinated 3 lighter
4 surprisingly 5 extraordinary 6 irrelevant
7 disagreement(s) 8 tolerant

Reading and Use of English: Transormations, page 66

1 am/'m looking forward to going

2 are/'re likely to take him

3 to set up

4 if/though they get on

5 come up with

6 split up with

Writing Part 2: Reports, page 66

2

They are too informal.

3

1 d 2 a 3 h 4 c 5 f 6 b 7 g 8 e

4

Wickwood's: it is inexpensive, enjoyable and a chance to have fun in a different atmosphere to that of the school.

Rington: it is relaxing and an ideal way to unwind after the exams. There is also a lot to do in the evening.

Unit 9 Mystery and imagination

Reading and Use of English: Gapped text, pages 68–69

1

1 D 2 G 3 B 4 A 5 F 6 C

2

a struck (infinitive: strike) b tricking c account for d glow e cited f log g flows h hover

3

1 tricked 2 cited 3 hovering 4 struck
5 accounted for 6 flows 7 glow/glowing 8 log

Vocabulary, pages 69–71

A Ways of looking

1 gazed 2 glared 3 stared 4 glimpse 5 glance
6 peered

B Phrasal verbs with *give*

1 c 2 e 3 a 4 g 5 b 6 d 7 f

C Expressions with *give*

1 example 2 lift 3 hand 4 permission
5 impression 6 call 7 idea 8 party

D Collocations

1 blank 2 baggy 3 nervous 4 luxurious
5 long-haul 6 spotty 7 sedentary 8 curly

E Word formation

1

Adjective	Adverb
1 humorous	humorously
2 passionate	passionately
3 financial	financially
4 angry	angrily
5 mysterious	mysteriously
6 natural	naturally
7 successful	successfully
8 attractive	attractively
9 enthusiastic	enthusiastically
10 offensive	offensively

2

1 successfully 2 unattractive 3 passionately
4 unenthusiastic 5 naturally 6 financial
7 angrily 8 inoffensive

Language focus, pages 71–73

A Modal verbs of speculation

1

1 might have left

2 correct

3 could/may/might have gone away

4 correct

5 correct

6 may/might not be the right size

7 can't/couldn't be going out with Sue

8 correct

9 He must have decided

10 correct

2

Possible answers:

1 He can't have slept very well.

He must have been working very hard.

He might have been driving all day.

2 She could be on a diet.

She may have split up with her boyfriend.

She might not be feeling very well.

3 The bus and train drivers might be on strike.

Everyone must have decided to drive to work today.

There may be a special event taking place.

4 It must be too hot for them.

You can't have watered them enough.

They might have some kind of disease.

5 Their son must have got into trouble again.

They might have caught the burglar that broke into their house.

They may have been looking for someone.

6 He might have found a job.

He must be going out with someone.

He could have won the lottery.

B Question tags

1 has he   2 aren't I   3 doesn't he   4 wouldn't you
5 didn't she   6 will you   7 will/would/can you
8 shall we   9 did it   10 do they

C Contrast linkers

1 B   2 B and C   3 A   4 C   5 A and B   6 A and C

Reading and Use of English: Multiple-choice cloze, page 73

1 A   2 C   3 D   4 A   5 C   6 B   7 B   8 A

Reading and Use of English: Open cloze, page 74

1 to   2 with   3 as   4 but   5 been   6 for   7 it
8 not

Writing: Essay, pages 74–75

2a

1 The style is formal.

2 The style is appropriate for the situation.

2b

1 result   2 hand   3 invest   4 too   5 whereas
6 opinion   7 more   8 pay   9 conclude   10 spend

3

Investment in libraries would help make them more dynamic and interactive, and therefore more popular.

4

on the other hand, Certainly, too, though, However, whereas, In my opinion, therefore, What is more, To conclude

Unit 10 Nothing but the truth

Reading and Use of English: Multiple matching, pages 76–77

1

1 D   2 B   3 C   4 D   5 A   6 B   7 C   8 D   9 A
10 C

2

1 a   2 c   3 e   4 b   5 f   6 d

3

1 snatched   2 squirt   3 waving   4 stalled
5 stuck   6 pointed

4

	a		b	
1	held		held	
2	makes		made	
3	got		got	
4	left		left	
5	having		had	

Vocabulary, pages 78–79

A Crime and punishment

1

1 arson   2 robbery   3 burglary   4 kidnap
5 blackmail

2

1 sentenced   2 given   3 ordered   4 acquitted

B Paraphrasing

1 into   2 from   3 at   4 in   5 on   6 on

C Phrasal verbs

1

1 up to   2 up with   3 out of   4 out with

2

1 told   2 nodding   3 giving   4 showing   5 took

Language focus, page 79

A Active and passive

1 was released, being found, did not/didn't commit or had not/hadn't committed

2 is being repaired, was told, won't/will not/wouldn't/would not be

3 have been asked, haven't/have not prepared

4 happened, were caught, were made, took

5 are produced, are sold, are exported

6 was given, died, stopped, hasn't/has not been fixed

7 is thought, was found, was walking

8 destroyed, haven't/have not done, be allowed

B Passive of reporting verbs

1 The family is known (by police) to run a number of illegal businesses.

2 Smith is thought to have broken into several homes.

3 She is expected to be given a life sentence.

4 Robinson is said to enjoy/be enjoying prison life.

5 Corelli is considered to have been the mastermind behind the crime.

Reading and Use of English: Multiple-choice cloze, page 80

1 B **2** B **3** D **4** A **5** D **6** C **7** B **8** C

Reading and Use of English: Open cloze, page 80

1 into **2** not **3** being **4** or **5** of **6** take **7** for **8** well

Reading and Use of English: Word formation, page 81

1 residential **2** reduction **3** robbery/robberies **4** effective **5** criminals **6** presence **7** invasion **8** evidence

Reading and Use of English: Transformations, page 81

1 not tall enough to be

2 there was too much

3 was made to eat on

4 is/'s being sorted out

5 been made up by

6 is said to be

Writing: Informal email, pages 82–83

1

Student B's answer would be given a higher mark. (see 2 below for reasons)

A Analysis

	A	B
1	no	yes
2	no	yes
3	yes	yes
4	no	yes
5	no	yes
6	no	yes
7	no	yes
8	no	yes
9	yes	yes
10	no	yes

B Accuracy

1

I **arrived** at the station

to catch the train

I **felt/was feeling** sad

I **had finished** my holiday

I **(had) decided** to go

make me **feel** happier

somebody **had stolen** it.

I **felt** sadder

2

at the station

because I had finished

I enjoyed the holiday

want to come home

the shop to buy

suitcase **on** the ground

paid the woman

to finish **a** holiday

C Addressing the reader

Did you get my postcard from Italy?

You'll never guess what happened to me after I'd posted it to you!

… you know how unfit I am!

You can imagine how relieved I felt.

How about you, Esther? Did anything exciting happen on your holiday? Write and tell me all about it.

Unit 11 What on earth's going on?

Reading and Use of English: Gapped text, pages 84–85

1

1 E **2** G **3** A **4** C **5** F **6** D

2a

1 go, goes **2** comes, come **3** run, runs **4** catch, catch

2b

1 comes complete with

2 it runs out of them

3 aims to go one better than

4 there's only one catch

5 it takes them two or three goes

Vocabulary, pages 85–87

A The environment

1

1 c **2** d **3** f **4** a **5** b **6** e

2

1 d **2** c **3** a **4** e **5** b **6** g **7** f

3

1 Exhaust fumes **2** oil slick **3** dog mess **4** greenhouse effect **5** power station

B The weather

Across	Down
1 drought	**2** hail
6 flood	**3** clouds
7 gale	**4** tidal
8 severe	**5** breeze
9 choppy	**6** forecast
11 fine	**10** pour
12 struck	
13 gust	

D Lexical phrases: revision

1 have/'ve put **2** taking **3** give **4** would/'d get
5 was put **6** to take **7** get **8** gave

Language focus, pages 87–88

A *So, neither* and *nor*

1

1 c **2** e **3** d **4** h **5** g **6** a **7** b **8** f

2

1 so is **2** neither/nor does **3** so are **4** so did
5 neither/nor will **6** so has **7** neither/nor would
8 so had

B Conditionals

1

1 'll/will buy, promise
2 hadn't/had not said, wouldn't/would not have got
3 sleeps, 's/is usually
4 'd/had gone, 'd/would have met
5 'll/will finish, win
6 press, underlines/'ll/will underline
7 were, 'd/would go
8 'll/will be, get
9 'd/had stopped, 'd/would be

2

Possible answers:

1 We would have gone sailing if there had been enough wind.
2 If I wasn't afraid of flying, we would go abroad on holiday.
3 If he hadn't broken his leg, he could drive.
4 I could have taken some photos if I had remembered to pack my camera.
5 If he had a suit, he would go to the wedding.
6 He wouldn't be feeling ill if he hadn't drunk so much last night.
7 She could have gone to university if she'd passed her exams.
8 If they'd watched the news, they would have heard about the earthquake.

3

Possible answers:

1 would probably miss my family
2 would try to improve the health system
3 I hadn't come to this school
4 they gave us an extra week's holiday in summer
5 I start revising now
6 I wouldn't be able to send emails to my friends in Australia.

Reading and Use of English: Multiple-choice cloze, page 89

1 B **2** C **3** B **4** D **5** B **6** A **7** D **8** A

Reading and Use of English: Open cloze, page 89

1 to **2** such **3** as **4** what **5** for **6** by
7 neither/not **8** at

Reading and Use of English: Transformations, page 90

1 's/has been put off
2 long as there isn't/is not
3 n't/not overslept, he would've/would have
4 's/has been raining heavily
5 herself/it and so did
6 more time/effort into

Writing: Article, pages 90–91

2

Questions to involve the reader: …what would be your favourite type of weather?, Glorious sunshine to sunbathe in?, Deep snow to ski in?, And what would you find it hard to put up with?, Who wouldn't feel bad-tempered by the end of it all?

A range of vocabulary related to the weather: glorious sunshine, deep snow, rain, fine or heavy, spitting or pouring, wet weather, cool, refreshing, the sun comes out, a shower, wind, blows

Elements of informal language: contractions: it's, there's, wouldn't, I'd; phrasal verbs: put up with, blown off, pulled off; linking words: And, But

Examples to illustrate a point: The rain on my face as I walk across the fields is cool and refreshing, Clothes are blown off washing lines, tiles are pulled off roofs, walking and cycling become very difficult

Adverbs expressing opinion or attitude: Surprisingly

4

Extract a: Writing competition (exercise **1**)

Consistent. An informal style

Extract b: People and places (exercise **3**)

Inconsistent. Begins with a formal style, but ends informally.

Extract c: Competition (exercise **3**)

Consistent. A neutral narrative style.

Unit 12 Looking after yourself

Reading and Use of English: Multiple choice, page 92

1

1 D 2 B 3 D 4 C 5 A 6 A

2

1 as 2 that 3 well 4 in 5 which 6 to
7 would

Vocabulary, pages 94–95

A Food and drink

1

1 eat, leave 2 Chewing 3 drink 4 swallowed
5 sip, gulp 6 bolted

2

1 greasy 2 rich 3 savoury 4 sour 5 sickly
6 crunchy 7 spicy 9 stodgy 9 bland

B Health

1 stiff 2 pressure, attack 3 runny 4 decay
5 sore 6 sprained 7 ache 8 black, bleed

C *Have, put, give* and *take*

1 e 2 d 3 g 4 a 5 b 6 h 7 f 8 c

Language focus, pages 95–96

A Reported speech

1 he was competing in a marathon the next/
following day

2 (that) she did aerobics

3 she was thinking of taking up jogging

4 if/whether they could give us

5 eating/(that) we (should) eat/us to eat

6 (her) students not to eat

7 if/whether they thought diets were

8 he had never needed to go on one

9 she had been/gone on a diet once

10 she would not do it again

11 liked/likes eating

B Reporting verbs

1 recommended 2 encouraged 3 invited
4 warned 5 reminded 6 suggested
7 recommended 8 told

C Countable and uncountable nouns

1 a 2 a large number 3 Every 4 suggestion,
accommodation 5 bar 6 few, much 7 no, a
few 8 little 9 any more 10 another

Reading and Use of English: Open cloze, page 96

1 to 2 for 3 before 4 However 5 no 6 who
7 on 8 instead

Reading and Use of English: Word formation, page 97

1 injury 2 difficulty/difficulties 3 weight 4 loss
5 Apparently 6 complications 7 improvement
8 truth

Reading and Use of English: Transformations, page 97

1 of/about the exact depth

2 had no choice (about) where

3 despite the late arrival

4 not give me (very) much

5 warned him not to

6 if/whether he had bought

Writing: Review, articles and informal letter, pages 98–99

A Planning

1 B 2 A 3 C

B Writing

1

1 c 2 a 3 b

Unit 13 Animal magic

Reading and Use of English: Gapped text, pages 100–101

1

1 E 2 A 3 C 4 G 5 B 6 F

2

1 with 2 on, of 3 over 4 out of 5 for
6 through 7 on 8 for

3

a took pity on

b put … out of his misery

c to do with

d midway through

e made a bid for freedom

f ran over

g on the lookout for

h take care of, care for

Vocabulary, pages 101–102

A The arts

Across	Down
1 sculptor	1 stage
4 play	2 priceless
6 scene	3 orchestra
7 house	4 portrait
8 landscape	5 composer
10 exhibition	7 hall
	9 cast

B Paraphrasing

1 face 2 doubt 3 question 4 criticism
5 sensation 6 attention 7 branch 8 fetch

C Parts of animals

1 fin 2 beak 3 mane 4 feather 5 hooves
6 claws 7 paw 8 fur 9 whiskers 10 gills

D Verbs followed by prepositions

1 on, for
2 for, from
3 for, of, for
4 for, on
5 for, on

Language focus, page 103

A Hypothetical situations

1

1 had 2 wouldn't make 3 had brought 4 knew
5 would stop 6 didn't tell 7 go 8 bought

2

Possible answers:

1 bought a watch
2 phoned before eight o'clock
3 would stop interrupting me
4 my exam were on a different day
5 I'd insured the video camera

B Prepositions and gerunds

1 instead of paying for
2 despite Naomi not feeling
3 in spite of being
4 result of Josh getting/coming
5 as well as taking

Reading and Use of English: Multiple-choice cloze, page 104

1 C 2 B 3 A 4 D 5 C 6 C 7 B 8 D

Reading and Use of English: Open cloze, page 104

1 for 2 be 3 as 4 which 5 No 6 Although/
Though/While/Whilst 7 there 8 in

Reading and Use of English: Word formation, page 105

1 considerable 2 decision 3 possibly 4 daily
5 residents 6 sight 7 irresponsible 8 beneficial

Reading and Use of English: Transformations, page 105

1 congratulated the players on winning
2 apologized (to Chrissie) for being
3 accused her of leaving
4 new about teachers coming
5 I had not/hadn't given
6 I'd/I had paid attention to

Writing, pages 106–107

A Ideas for Part 1

1

b ✓ c ✓

2

a ✓ b ✗ c ✓

3

a ✗ b ✓ c ✗

B Language preparation

1

1 aim of this report
2 my opinion
3 have no experience of
4 that struck me
5 people believe that
6 a great deal about
7 I like most about her
8 express an interest
9 option would be to
10 a large number of

2

1 3 2 1 3 2 4 4 5 1 6 3 7 4 8 2 9 3 10 1

Unit 14 Mind your language

Reading and Use of English: Multiple choice, pages 108–109

1

1 C 2 A 3 D 4 D 5 C 6 A

2

1 anxiety 2 anger 3 irritation 4 ability
5 alertness 6 confidence 7 weight
8 subtlety/subtleties 9 weakness 10 variety
11 credibility 12 certainty/certainties
13 persistence 14 complication 15 complaint
16 hunger

Vocabulary, pages 109–110

A Phrasal verbs with *turn*

1 down 2 up 3 into 4 on 5 out 6 off

B Expressions with *turn*

1 c 2 e 3 a 4 b 5 h 6 g 7 d 8 f

C Revision

1 getting, do 2 doing, put 3 putting, get
4 make, made 5 gives, taking

D Expressions with *make* and *do*

2 d does, (to) do
3 f do, made
4 g do, do
5 b make, do
6 c made, do
7 a does/is doing, makes/is making/has made

149

Language focus, pages 111–112

A Compound adjectives

1 a Spanish-made car
2 a Russian-speaking guide
3 a London-based company
4 a French-owned supermarket chain
5 a ten-day cruise
6 a 29-year-old woman
7 a 650-page book
8 a four-hour film
9 a three-day conference

B Expressing purpose

1

2 e 3 a 4 f 5 h 6 i 7 b 8 g 9 d

2

2 so that she wouldn't/so as not to/in order not to speak any Spanish.
3 in case it was cold there.
4 in case she didn't understand any English.
5 in order to see/so as to see/so that she could see the rest of the country.
6 so that she could read/in order to/so as to (be able to) read about the different places before visiting them.
7 so that her parents wouldn't worry about her. (in case her parents were worried about her).
8 so that she doesn't/won't forget/in order not to forget/so as not to forget what she learnt.
9 in case she goes back to Ireland next year.

C Ability

1 correct
2 Trevor was able to mend/managed to mend/succeeded in mending (or must have mended)
3 correct
4 correct
5 correct
6 I've never been able to swim
7 he's incapable of organizing
8 correct
9 she won't be able to come/she can't come
10 They didn't succeed in getting

Reading and Use of English: Open cloze, page 112

1 turned 2 into 3 instead 4 who 5 by
6 more 7 to 8 In

Reading and Use of English: Multiple-choice cloze, page 113

1 B 2 C 3 D 4 A 5 B 6 D 7 B 8 A

Reading and Use of English: Word formation, page 113

1 inaccessible 2 written 3 suspicious
4 endless 5 eventful 6 political
7 disappearance 8 knowledge

Reading and Use of English: Transformations, page 114

1 did not/didn't succeed in reaching
2 is capable of running
3 so (that) he would not/wouldn't or so as not to
4 not/n't making any effort to/making no effort to
5 in case she turns
6 made two unsuccessful

Listening bank

Unit 1

Listening: Multiple matching, page 116

1

Speaker 1 school pupil Speaker 2 doctor
Speaker 3 college student Speaker 4 teacher
Speaker 5 manager

2

Speaker 1 G Speaker 2 B Speaker 3 E
Speaker 4 D Speaker 5 F

3a

1 a set	b Setting
2 a turned	b turned
3 a looking	b looked
4 a made	b made

3b

1 … it's the best decision I've ever made.
2 … no one made any fuss about it.
3 Setting up a business in another country is not an easy thing to do!
4 … it turned out to be a great success.
5 I haven't looked back!

Unit 2

Listening: Sentence completion, page 117

1

1 sporting ability 2 athlete 3 10,000/ten thousand 4 two/2 5 distractions 6 street
7 coach 8 Open 9 Australia 10 superstition(s)

2

1 for 2 in 3 in 4 to 5 to 6 on

Unit 3

Listening: Multiple choice, page 118

1
1 C **2** A **3** C **4** A **5** C **6** A **7** B
2
1 c **2** f **3** d **4** a **5** b **6** e

Unit 4

Listening: Multiple choice, page 119

1 C **2** B **3** B **4** B **5** C **6** B **7** B **8** B

Unit 5

Listening: Sentence completion, page 120

1
1 passion **2** Rainbows **3** (only) three/3
4 routine **5** morning(s) **6** café **7** fountain pen
8 writer's block **9** different **10** five/5
2
1 put **2** fooled **3** set **4** write **5** run **6** go

Unit 6

Listening: Multiple matching, page 121

1
1 C **2** F **3** H **4** E **5** B
2
1 c **2** e **3** a **4** f **5** d **6** b

Unit 7

Listening: Multiple choice, page 122

1 C **2** B **3** B **4** B **5** A **6** C **7** B

Unit 8

Listening: Multiple choice, page 123

1 B **2** A **3** C **4** B **5** A **6** B **7** C **8** A

Unit 9

Listening: Sentence completion, page 124

1
1 adventure **2** 1887 **3** England **4** mother
5 56/fifty-six **6** 21st century **7** *The Final Problem*
8 The Ghost Club **9** article **10** (rose) garden
2
1 when **2** both **3** the time, However
4 As well as **5** Although **6** eventually

Unit 10

Listening: Multiple choice, page 125

1 B **2** B **3** A **4** A **5** C **6** C **7** C

Unit 11

Listening: Multiple choice, page 126

1 A **2** B **3** B **4** B **5** A **6** A **7** C **8** C

Unit 12

Listening: Multiple matching, page 127

1
1 C **2** E **3** H **4** B **5** F
2a
1 looking **2** working **3** get **4** made **5** turned
6 got
2b
b got fed up with
c made up
d looking after
e working my way through
f turned out

Unit 13

Listening: Sentence completion, page 128

1
1 millionaires' houses **2** photographs **3** (the)
Internet **4** realistic **5** the sixteenth/16th century
6 churches **7** Second World War **8** Picasso
9 19/nineteen **10** (Northern) Italy
2
1 complicated **2** religious **3** influential
4 realistic **5** traditional **6** prestigious
7 three-dimensional

Unit 14

Listening: Multiple matching, page 129

1
1 H **2** G **3** E **4** A **5** D
2
1 b **2** c **3** f **4** a **5** e **6** d